PRIMARY

Problem-solving in mathematics

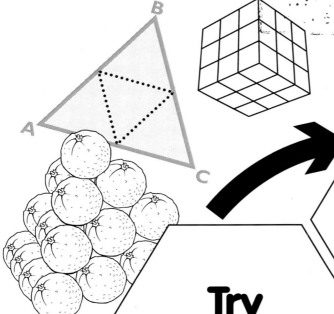

Analyse
the problem

Try
a solution strategy

Explore
means to a solution

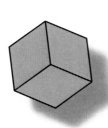

George Booker and Denise Bond

Reaside Academy
Tresco Close
Frankley
Birmingham
B45 0HY
Tel: 0121 675 7235
Fax: 0121 675 1958

6033UK

46/5

Problem-solving in mathematics
(Book D)

Published by R.I.C. Publications® 2008

Republished under licence by Prim-Ed Publishing 2009

Copyright© George Booker and Denise Bond 2007

ISBN 978-1-84654-185-8

PR–6033

Titles available in this series:

Problem-solving in mathematics *(Book A)*
Problem-solving in mathematics *(Book B)*
Problem-solving in mathematics *(Book C)*
Problem-solving in mathematics *(Book D)*
Problem-solving in mathematics *(Book E)*
Problem-solving in mathematics *(Book F)*
Problem-solving in mathematics *(Book G)*

Internet websites

In some cases, websites or specific URLs may be recommended. While these are checked and rechecked at the time of publication, the publisher has no control over any subsequent changes which may be made to webpages. It is *strongly* recommended that the class teacher checks *all* URLs before allowing pupils to access them.

View all pages online

Website: www.prim-ed.com

Books A–G of *Problem-solving in mathematics* have been developed to provide a rich resource for teachers of pupils from the early years to the end of primary school and into secondary school. The series of problems, discussions of ways to understand what is being asked and means of obtaining solutions have been built up to improve the problem-solving performance and persistence of all pupils. It is a fundamental belief of the authors that it is critical that pupils and teachers engage with a few complex problems over an extended period rather than spend a short time on many straightforward 'problems' or exercises. In particular, it is essential to allow pupils time to review and discuss what is required in the problem-solving process before moving to another and different problem. This book includes extensive ideas for extending problems and solution strategies to assist teachers in implementing this vital aspect of mathematics in their classrooms. Also, the problems have been constructed and selected over many years' experience with pupils at all levels of mathematical talent and persistence, as well as in discussions with teachers in classrooms, professional learning and university settings.

Problem-solving does not come easily to most people, so learners need many experiences engaging with problems if they are to develop this crucial ability. As they grapple with problem, meaning and find solutions, pupils will learn a great deal about mathematics and mathematical reasoning; for instance, how to organise information to uncover meanings and allow connections among the various facets of a problem to become more apparent, leading to a focus on organising what needs to be done rather than simply looking to apply one or more strategies. In turn, this extended thinking will help pupils make informed choices about events that impact on their lives and to interpret and respond to the decisions made by others at school, in everyday life and in further study.

Pupil and teacher pages

The pupil pages present problems chosen with a particular problem-solving focus and draw on a range of mathematical understandings and processes. For each set of related problems, teacher notes and discussion are provided, as well as indications of how particular problems can be examined and solved. Answers to the more straightforward problems and detailed solutions to the more complex problems

ensure appropriate explanations. The use of the pages foster discussion among pupils and suggest ways in which problems can be extended. Related problems occur on one or more pages that extend the problem's ideas, the solution processes and pupils' understanding of the range of ways to come to terms with what problems are asking.

At the top of each teacher page, there is a statement that highlights the particular thinking that the problems will demand, together with an indication of the mathematics that might be needed and a list of materials that could be used in seeking a solution. A particular focus for the page or set of three pages of problems then expands on these aspects. Each book is organised so that when a problem requires complicated strategic thinking, two or three problems occur on one page (supported by a teacher page with detailed discussion) to encourage pupils to find a solution together with a range of means that can be followed. More often, problems are grouped as a series of three interrelated pages where the level of complexity gradually increases, while the associated teacher page examines one or two of the problems in depth and highlights how the other problems might be solved in a similar manner.

Each teacher page concludes with two further aspects critical to successful teaching of problem-solving. A section on likely difficulties points to reasoning and content inadequacies that experience has shown may well impede pupils' success. In this way, teachers can be on the look out for difficulties and be prepared to guide pupils past these potential pitfalls. The final section suggests extensions to the problems to enable teachers to provide several related experiences with problems of these kinds in order to build a rich array of experiences with particular solution methods; for example, the numbers, shapes or measurements in the original problems might change but leave the means to a solution essentially the same, or the context may change while the numbers, shapes or measurements remain the same. Then numbers, shapes or measurements and the context could be changed to see how the pupils handle situations that appear different but are essentially the same as those already met and solved. Other suggestions ask pupils to make and pose their own problems, investigate and present background to the problems or topics to the class, or consider solutions at a more general level (possibly involving verbal descriptions and eventually pictorial or symbolic arguments). In this way, not only are pupils' ways of thinking extended but the problems written on one page are used to produce several more problems that utilise the same approach.

Mathematics and language

The difficulty of the mathematics gradually increases over the series, largely in line with what is taught at the various year levels, although problem-solving both challenges at the point of the mathematics that is being learned as well as provides insights and motivation for what might be learned next. For example, the computation required gradually builds from additive thinking, using addition and subtraction separately and together, to multiplicative thinking, where multiplication and division are connected conceptions. More complex interactions of these operations build up over the series as the operations are used to both come to terms with problems' meanings and to achieve solutions. Similarly, two-dimensional geometry is used at first but extended to more complex uses over the range of problems, then joined by interaction with three-dimensional ideas. Measurement, including chance and data, also extends over the series from length to perimeter, and from area to surface area and volume, drawing on the relationships among these concepts to organise solutions as well as giving an understanding of the metric system. Time concepts range from interpreting timetables using 12-hour and 24-hour clocks while investigations related to mass rely on both the concept itself and practical measurements.

The language in which the problems are expressed is relatively straightforward, although this too increases in complexity and length of expression across the books in terms of both the context in which the problems are set and the mathematical content that is required. It will always be a challenge for some pupils to 'unpack' the meaning from a worded problem, particularly as problems' context, information and meanings expand. This ability is fundamental to the nature of mathematical problem-solving and needs to be built up with time and experiences rather than be diminished or left out of the problems' situations. One reason for the suggestion that pupils work in groups is to allow them to share and assist each other with the tasks of discerning meanings and ways to tackle the ideas in complex problems through discussion, rather than simply leaping into the first ideas that come to mind (leaving the full extent of the problem unrealised).

An approach to solving problems

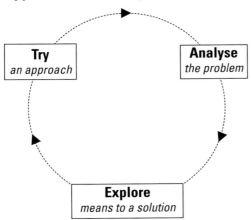

The careful, gradual development of an ability to analyse problems for meaning, organising information to make it meaningful and to make the connections among them more meaningful in order to suggest a way forward to a solution is fundamental to the approach taken with this series, from the first book to the last. At first, materials are used explicitly to aid these meanings and connections; however, in time they give way to diagrams, tables and symbols as understanding and experience of solving complex, engaging problems increases. As the problem forms expand, the range of methods to solve problems is carefully extended, not only to allow pupils to successfully solve the many

types of problems, but also to give them a repertoire of solution processes that they can consider and draw on when new situations are encountered. In turn, this allows them to explore one or other of these approaches to see whether each might furnish a likely result. In this way, when they try a particular method to solve a new problem, experience and analysis of the particular situation assists them to develop a full solution.

Not only is this model for the problem-solving process helpful in solving problems, it also provides a basis for pupils to discuss their progress and solutions and determine whether or not they have fully answered a question. At the same time, it guides teacher questions of pupils and provides a means of seeing underlying mathematical difficulties and ways in which problems can be adapted to suit particular needs and extensions. Above all, it provides a common framework for discussions between a teacher and group or whole class to focus on the problem-solving process rather than simply on the solution of particular problems. Indeed, as Alan Schoenfeld, in Steen L (Ed) *Mathematics and democracy* (2001), states so well, in problem-solving:

getting the answer is only the beginning rather than the end ... an ability to communicate thinking is equally important.

We wish all teachers and pupils who use these books success in fostering engagement with problem-solving and building a greater capacity to come to terms with and solve mathematical problems at all levels.

George Booker and Denise Bond

CONTENTS

Problem-solving and mathematical thinking

> *By learning problem-solving in mathematics, pupils should acquire ways of thinking, habits of persistence and curiosity, and confidence in unfamiliar situations that will serve them well outside the mathematics classroom. In everyday life and in the workplace, being a good problem solver can lead to great advantages.*
>
> **NCTM principles and standards for school mathematics**
> **(2000, p. 52)**

Problem-solving lies at the heart of mathematics. New mathematical concepts and processes have always grown out of problem situations and pupils' problem-solving capabilities develop from the very beginning of mathematics learning. A need to solve a problem can motivate pupils to acquire new ways of thinking as well as to come to terms with concepts and processes that might not have been adequately learned when first introduced. Even those who can calculate efficiently and accurately are ill prepared for a world where new and adaptable ways of thinking are essential if they are unable to identify which information or processes are needed.

On the other hand, pupils who can analyse problem meanings, explore means to a solution and carry out a plan to solve mathematical problems have acquired deeper and more useful knowledge than simply being able to complete calculations, name shapes, use formulas to make measurements or determine measures of chance and data. It is critical that mathematics teaching focuses on enabling all pupils to become both able and willing to engage with and solve mathematical problems.

Well-chosen problems encourage deeper exploration of mathematical ideas, build persistence and highlight the need to understand thinking strategies, properties and relationships. They also reveal the central role of *sense making* in mathematical thinking—not only to evaluate the need for assessing the reasonableness of an answer or solution, but also the need to consider the inter-relationships among the information provided with a problem situation. This may take the form of number sense, allowing numbers to be represented in various ways and operations to be interconnected; through spatial sense that allows the visualisation of a problem in both its parts and whole; to a sense of measurement across length, area, volume and chance and data.

Problem-solving

A problem is a task or situation for which there is no immediate or obvious solution, so that *problem-solving* refers to the processes used when engaging with this task. When problem-solving, pupils engage with situations for which a solution strategy is not immediately obvious, drawing on their understanding of concepts and processes they have already met, and will often develop new understandings and ways of thinking as they move towards a solution. It follows that a task that is a problem for one pupil may not be a problem for another and that a situation that is a problem at one level will only be an exercise or routine application of a known means to a solution at a later time.

A large number of tourists visited Uluru during 2007. There were twice as many visitors in 2007 than in 2003 and 6530 more visitors in 2007 than in 2006. If there were 298 460 visitors in 2003, how many were there in 2006?

For a pupil aged 7-10 years, sorting out the information to see how the number of visitors each year are linked is a considerable task and then there is a need to use multiplication and subtraction with large numbers. For a pupil in later primary years, an ability to see how the problem is structured and familiarity with computation could lead them to use a calculator, key in the numbers and operation in an appropriate order and readily obtain the answer:

$$298460 \times 2 - 6530 = 590390$$

590 390 tourists visited Uluru in 2006

As the world in which we live becomes ever more complex, the level of mathematical thinking and problem-solving needed in life and in the workplace has increased considerably. Those who understand and can use the mathematics they have learned will have opportunities opened to them that those who do not develop these ways of thinking will not. To enable pupils to thrive in this changing world, attitudes and ways of knowing that enable them to deal with new or unfamiliar tasks are now as essential as the procedures that have always been used to handle familiar operations readily and efficiently. Such an attitude needs to develop from the beginning of mathematics learning as pupils form beliefs about meaning, the notion of taking control over the activities they engage with and the results they obtain, and as they build an inclination to try different approaches. In other words, pupils need to see mathematics as a way of thinking rather than a means of providing answers to be judged right or wrong by a teacher, textbook or some other external authority. They need to be led to focus on means of solving problems rather than on particular answers so that they understand the need to determine the meaning of a problem before beginning to work on a solution.

In a car race, Jordan started in fourth place. During the race, he was passed by six cars. How many cars does he need to pass to win the race?

In order to solve this problem, it is not enough to simply use the numbers that are given. Rather, an analysis of the race situation is needed first to see that when Jordan started there were 3 cars ahead of him. When another 6 cars passed him there were now 9 ahead of him. If he is to win, he needs to pass all 9 cars. The 4 and 6 implied in the problem were not used at all! Rather, a diagram or the use of materials is needed first to interpret the situation and then see how a solution can be obtained.

However, many pupils feel inadequate when they encounter problem-solving questions. They seem to have no idea of how to go about finding a solution and are unable to draw on the competencies they have learned in number, space and measurement. Often these difficulties stem from underdeveloped concepts for the operations, spatial thinking and measurement processes. They may also involve an underdeveloped capacity to read problems for meaning and a tendency to be led astray by the wording or numbers in a problem situation. Their approach may then simply be to try a series of guesses or calculations rather than consider using a diagram or materials to come to terms with what the problem is asking and using a systematic approach to organise the information given and required in the task. It is this ability to analyse problems that is the key to problem-solving, enabling decisions to be made about which mathematical processes to use, which information is needed and which ways of proceeding are likely to lead to a solution.

Making sense in mathematics

Making sense of the mathematics being developed and used needs to be seen as the central concern of learning. This is important, not only in coming to terms with problems and means to solutions, but also in terms of putting meanings, representations and relationships in mathematical ideas to the forefront of thinking about and dealing with mathematics. Making sensible interpretations of any results and determining which of several possibilities is more or equally likely is critical in problem-solving.

Number sense, which involves being able to work with numbers comfortably and competently, is important in many aspects of problem-solving, in making judgments, interpreting information and communicating ways of thinking. It is based on a full understanding of numeration concepts such as zero, place value and the renaming of numbers in equivalent forms, so that 207 can be seen as 20 tens and 7 ones as well as 2 hundreds and 7 ones (or that $\frac{5}{2}$, 2.5 and $2\frac{1}{2}$ are all names for the same fraction amount). Automatic, accurate access to basic facts also underpins number sense, not as an end in itself, but rather as a means of combining with numeration concepts to allow manageable mental strategies and fluent processes for larger numbers. Well-understood concepts for the operations are essential in allowing relationships within a problem to be revealed and taken into account when framing a solution.

Number sense requires:

- understanding relationships among numbers
- appreciating the relative size of numbers
- a capacity to calculate and estimate mentally
- fluent processes for larger numbers and adaptive use of calculators
- an inclination to use understanding and facility with numeration and computation in flexible ways.

The following problem highlights the importance of these understandings.

There were 317 people at the New Year's Eve party on 31 December. If each table could seat 5 couples, how many tables were needed?

Reading the problem carefully shows that each table seats five couples or 10 people. At first glance, this problem might be solved using division; however, this would result in a decimal fraction, which is not useful in dealing with people seated at tables:

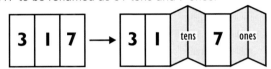

$10\overline{)317}$ is 31.7

In contrast, a full understanding of numbers allows 317 to be renamed as 31 tens and 7 ones:

$$\boxed{3}\boxed{1}\boxed{7} \rightarrow \boxed{3}\boxed{1}\boxed{\text{tens}}\boxed{7}\boxed{\text{ones}}$$

This provides for all the people at the party and analysis of the number 317 shows that there needs to be at least 32 tables for everyone to have a seat and allow party goers to move around and sit with others during the evening. Understanding how to *rename* a number has provided a direct solution without any need for computation. It highlights how coming to terms with a problem and integrating this with number sense provides a means of solving the problem more directly and allows an appreciation of what the solution might mean.

Spatial sense is equally important as information is frequently presented in visual formats that need to be interpreted and processed, while the use of diagrams is often essential in developing conceptual understanding across all aspects of mathematics. Using diagrams, placing information in tables or depicting a systematic way of dealing with the various possibilities in a problem assist in visualising what is happening. It can be a very powerful tool in coming to terms with the information in a problem and it provides insight into ways to proceed to a solution.

Spatial sense involves:

- a capacity to visualise shapes and their properties
- determining relationships among shapes and their properties
- linking two-dimensional and three-dimensional representations
- presenting and interpreting information in tables and lists
- an inclination to use diagrams and models to visualise problem situations and applications in flexible ways.

The following problem shows how these understandings can be used.

A small sheet of paper has been folded in half and then cut along the fold to make two rectangles.

The perimeter of each rectangle is 18 cm.

What was the perimeter of the original square sheet of paper?

Reading the problem carefully and analysing the diagram shows that the length of the longer side of the rectangle is the same as one side of the square while the other side of the rectangle is half this length. Another way to obtain this insight is to make a square, fold it in half along the cutting line and then fold it again. This shows that the large square is made up of four smaller squares:

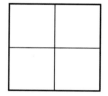

Since each rectangle contains two small squares, the perimeter of the rectangle, 18 cm, is the same as 6 sides of the smaller square, so the side of the small square is 3 cm. The perimeter of the large square is made of 8 of these small sides, so is 24 cm.

Similar thinking is used with arrangements of two-dimensional and three-dimensional shapes and in visualising how they can fit together or be taken apart.

Many dice are made in the shape of a cube with arrangements of dots on each square face so that the sum of the dots on opposite faces is always 7. An arrangement of squares that can be folded to make a cube is called a net of a cube.

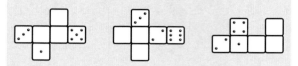

Which of these arrangements of squares forms a net for the dice?

Greengrocers often stack fruit as a pyramid.

How many oranges are in this stack?

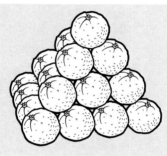

Measurement sense is dependent on both number sense and spatial sense as attributes that are one-, two- or three-dimensional are quantified to provide both exact and approximate measures and allow comparison. Many measurements use aspects of space (length, area, volume), while others use numbers on a scale (time, mass, temperature). Money can be viewed as a measure of value and uses numbers more directly, while practical activities such as map reading and determining angles require a sense of direction as well as gauging measurement. The coordination of the thinking for number and space, along with an understanding of how the metric system builds on place value, zero and renaming, is critical in both building measurement understanding and using it to come to terms with and solve many practical problems and applications.

Measurement sense includes:

- understanding how numeration and computation underpin measurement
- extending relationships from number understandings to the metric system
- appreciating the relative size of measurements
- a capacity to use calculators, mental or written processes for exact and approximate calculations
- an inclination to use understanding and facility with measurements in flexible ways.

The following problem shows how these understandings can be used.

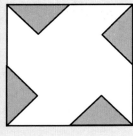

A city square has an area of 160 m². Four small triangular garden beds are constructed from each corner to the midpoints of the sides of the square. What is the area of each garden bed?

Reading the problem carefully shows that there are 4 garden beds and each of them takes up the same proportions of the whole square. A quick look at the area of the square shows that there will not be an exact number of metres along one side. Some further thinking will be needed to determine the area of each garden bed.

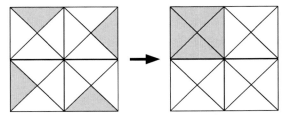

If the midpoints of each side are drawn across the square, four smaller squares are formed and each garden bed takes up $\frac{1}{4}$ of a small square. Four of the garden beds will have the same area of one small square. Since area of the small square is $\frac{1}{4}$ the area of the large square, the area of one small square is 40 m² and the area of each triangular garden bed is 10 m².

An understanding of the problem situation given by a diagram has been integrated with spatial thinking and a capacity to calculate mentally with simple fractions to provide an appropriate solution. Both spatial sense and number sense have been used to understand the problem and suggest a means to a solution.

Data sense is an outgrowth of measurement sense and refers to an understanding of the way number sense, spatial sense and a sense of measurement work together to deal with situations where patterns need to be discerned among data or when likely outcomes need to be analysed. This can occur among frequencies in data or possibilities in chance.

Data sense involves:

- understanding how numeration and computation underpin the analysis of data
- appreciating the relative likelihood of outcomes
- a capacity to use calculators or mental and written processes for exact and approximate calculations
- presenting and interpreting data in tables and graphs
- an inclination to use understanding and facility with number combinations and arrangements in flexible ways.

The following problem shows how these understandings can be used.

You are allowed 3 scoops of ice-cream: 1 chocolate, 1 vanilla and 1 strawberry. How many different ways can the scoops be placed on a cone?

There are six possibilities for placing the scoops of ice-cream on a cone. Systematically treating the possible placements one at a time highlights how the use of a diagram can account for all possible arrangements.

Patterning is another critical aspect of sense making in mathematics. Often a problem calls on discerning a pattern in the placement of materials, the numbers involved in the situation or the possible arrangements of data or outcomes so as to determine a likely solution. Being able to see patterns is also very helpful in getting a solution more immediately or understanding whether or not a solution is complete.

A farmer had emus and alpacas in one paddock. When she counted, there were 38 heads and 100 legs. How many emus and how many alpacas are in the paddock?

There are 38 emus and alpacas. Emus have 2 legs. Alpacas have 4 legs.

Number of alpacas	Number of emus	Number of legs
4	34	84 – too few
8	30	92 – too few
10	28	96 – too few
12	26	100

There are 12 alpacas and 26 emus.

As more experience in solving problems is gained, an ability to see patterns in what is occurring will also allow solutions to be obtained more directly and help in seeing the relationship between a new problem and one that has been solved previously. It is this ability to relate problem types, even when the context appears to be quite different, that often distinguishes a good problem-solver from one who is more hesitant.

Building a problem-solving process

While the teaching of problem-solving has often centred on the use of particular strategies that could apply to various classes of problems, many pupils are unable to access and use these strategies to solve problems outside of the teaching situations in which they were introduced. Rather than acquire a process for solving problems, they may attempt to memorise a set of procedures and view mathematics as a set of learned rules where success follows the use of the right procedure to the numbers given in the problem. Any use of strategies may be based on familiarity, personal preference or recent exposure rather than through a consideration of the problem to be solved. A pupil may even feel it is sufficient to have only one strategy and that the strategy should work all of the time; and if it doesn't, then the problem 'can't be done'.

In contrast, observation of successful problem-solvers shows that their success depends more on an analysis of the problem itself—what is being asked, what information might be used, what answer might be likely and so on—so that a particular approach is used only after the intent of the problem is determined. Establishing the meaning of the problem before any plan is drawn up or work on a solution begins is critical. Pupils need to see that discussion about the problem's meaning, and the ways of obtaining a solution, must take precedence over a focus on 'the answer'. Using collaborative groups when problem-solving, rather than tasks assigned individually, is an approach that helps to develop this disposition.

Looking at a problem and working through what is needed to solve it will shed light on the problem-solving process.

On Saturday, Peta went to the shopping centre to buy a new outfit to wear at her friend's birthday party. She spent half of her money on a dress and then one-third of what she had left on a pair of sandals. After her purchases, she had £60.00 left in her purse. How much money did she have to start with?

By carefully reading the problem, it can be determined that Peta had an original amount of money to spend. She spent some on a dress and some on shoes and then had £60.00 left. All of the information required to solve the problem is available and no further information is needed. The question at the end asks how much money did she start with, but really the problem is how much did she spend on the dress and then on the sandals.

The discussion of this problem has served to identify the key element within the problem-solving process; it is necessary to analyse the problem to unfold its meanings and discover what needs to be considered.

INTRODUCTION

What the problem is asking is rarely found in the question in the problem statement. Instead, it is necessary to look below the 'surface level' of the problem and come to terms with the problem's structure. Reading the problem aloud, thinking of previous problems and other similar problems, selecting important information from the problem that may be useful, and discussion of the problem's meaning are all essential.

The next step is to explore possible ways to solve the problem. If the analysis stage has been completed, then ways in which the problem might be solved will emerge. It is here that strategies, and how they might be useful to solving a problem, can arise. However, most problems can be solved in a variety of ways, using different approaches, and a pupil needs to be encouraged to select a method that make sense and appears achievable to him or her.

Ways that may come to mind during the analysis include:

- *Materials* – Base 10 materials could be used to represent the money spent and to help the pupil work backwards through the problem from when Peta had £60.00 left.
- *Try and adjust* – Select an amount that Peta might have taken shopping, try it in the context of the question, examine the resulting amounts, and then adjust them, if necessary, until £60.00 is the result.
- *Backtrack using the numbers* – The sandals were one-third of what was left after the dress, so the £60.00 would be two-thirds of what was left. Together, these two amounts would match the cost of the dress.
- *Use a diagram* to represent the information in the problem.
- *Think of a similar problem* – For example, it is like the car race problem in that the relative portions (places) are known and the final result (money left, winning position) are given.

Now *one* of the possible means to a solution can be selected to try. Backtracking shows that £60 was two-thirds of what she had left, so the sandals (which are one-third of what she had left) must have cost £30.

Together, these are half of what Peta took, which is also the cost of the dress. As the dress cost £90, Peta took £180 to spend.

Materials could also have been used to work with backwards: 6 tens represent the £60 left, so the sandals would cost 3 tens and the dress 9 tens—she took 18 tens or £180 shopping.

Another way to solve this problem is with a diagram. If we use a rectangle to represent how much money Peta took with her, we can show by shading how much she spent on a dress and sandals:

Total amount available to spend:

She spent half of her money on a dress.

She then spent one-third of what she had left on sandals, which has minimised and simplified the calculations.

At this point she had £60 left, so the two-unshaded parts must be worth £60 or £30 per part—which has again minimised and simplified the calculations.

	£30	£30

Each of the six equal parts represents £30, so Peta took £180 to spend.

Having tried an idea, an answer needs to be analysed in the light of the problem in case another solution is required. It is essential to compare an answer back to the original analysis of the problem to determine whether the solution obtained is reasonable and answers the problem. It will also raise the question as to whether other answers exist, and even whether there might be other solution strategies. In this way the process is cyclic and should the answer be unreasonable, then the process would need to begin again.

We believe that Peta took £180 to shop with. She spent half (or £90) on a dress, leaving £90. She spent one-third of the £90 on sandals (£30), leaving £60. Looking again at the problem, we see that this is correct and the diagram has provided a direct means to the solution that has minimised and simplified the calculations.

Thinking about how the various ways this problem was solved highlights the key elements within the problem-solving process. When starting the process, it is necessary to *analyse* the problem to unfold its layers, discover its structure and what the problem was really asking. Next, all possible ways to solve the problem were *explored* before one, or a combination of ways, was/were selected to *try*. Finally, once something was tried, it was important to check the solution in relation to the problem to see if the solution was reasonable. This process highlights the cyclic nature of problem-solving and brings to the fore the importance of understanding the problem (and its structure) before proceeding. This process can be summarised as:

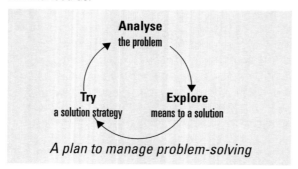

A plan to manage problem-solving

This model for problem-solving provides pupils with a means of talking about the steps they engage with whenever they have a problem to solve: Discussing how they initially analysed the problem, explored various ways that might provide a solution, and then tried one or more possible solution paths to obtain a solution—that they analysed for completeness and sense making—reinforces the very methods that will give them success on future problems. This process brings to the fore the importance of understanding the problem and its structure before proceeding.

Further, returning to an analysis of any answers and solution strategies highlights the importance of reflecting on what has been done. Taking time to reflect on any plans drawn up, processes followed and strategies used brings out the significance of coming to terms with the nature of the problem, as well as the value and applicability of particular approaches that might be used with other problems. Thinking of how a related problem was solved is often the key to solving another problem at a later stage. It allows the thinking to be 'carried over' to the new situation in a way that simply trying to think of the strategy used often fails to reveal. Analysing problems in this way also highlights that a problem is not solved until any answer obtained can be justified. Learning to reflect on the *whole* process leads to the development of a deeper understanding of problem-solving, and time must be allowed for reflection and discussion to fully build mathematical thinking.

Managing a problem-solving programme

Teaching problem-solving differs from many other aspects of mathematics in that collaborative work can be more productive than individual work. Pupils who may be tempted to quickly give up when working on their own can be led to see ways of proceeding when discussing a problem in a group. Therefore building greater confidence in their capacity to solve problems and learning the value of persisting with a problem in order to tease out what is required. What is discussed with their peers is more likely to be recalled when other problems are met while the observations made in the group increase the range of approaches that a pupil can access. Thus, time has to be allowed for discussion and exploration rather than ensuring that pupils spend 'time on task' as for routine activities.

Correct answers that fully solve a problem are always important, but developing a capacity to use an effective problem-solving process needs to be the highest priority. A pupil who has an answer should be encouraged to discuss his or her solution

with others who believe they have a solution, rather than tell his or her answer to another pupil or simply move on to another problem. In particular, explaining to others why he or she believes an answer is reasonable, as well as why it provides a solution, gets other pupils to focus on the entire problem-solving process rather than just quickly getting an answer.

Expressing an answer in a sentence that relates to the question stated in the problem also encourages reflection on what was done and ensures that the focus is on solving the problem rather than providing an answer. These aspects of the teaching of problem-solving should then be taken further, as particular groups discuss their solutions with the whole class and all pupils are able to participate in the discussion of the problem. In this way, problem-solving as a way of thinking comes to the fore, rather than focusing on the answers to a series of problems that some pupils see as the main aim of their mathematical activities.

Questions need to encourage pupils to explore possible means to a solution and try one or more of them, rather than point to a particular procedure. It can also assist pupils to see how to progress their thinking, rather than get in a loop where the same steps are repeated over and over. However, while having too many questions that focus on the way to a solution may end up removing the problem-solving aspect from the question, having too few may cause pupils to become frustrated with the task and think that it is beyond them. Pupils need to experience the challenge of problem-solving and gain pleasure from working through the process that leads to a full solution. Taking time to listen to pupils as they try out their ideas, without comment or without directing them to a particular strategy, is also important. Listening provides a sense of how pupils' problem solving is developing, as assessing this aspect of mathematics can be difficult. After all, solving one problem will not necessarily lead to success on the next problem, nor will a difficulty with a particular problem mean that the problems that follow will also be as challenging.

A teacher may also need to extend or adapt a given problem to ensure the problem-solving process is understood and can be used in other situations, instead of moving on to another different problem in the way that one example or topic shifts to another in other parts of mathematics learning. This can help pupils to understand the significance of asking questions of a problem, as well as seeing how a way of thinking can be adapted to other related problems. Having pupils engage in this process of problem posing is another way of both assessing and bringing them to terms with the overall process of solving problems.

Building a problem-solving process

The cyclical model, *Analyse–Explore–Try*, provides a very helpful means of organising and discussing possible solutions. However, care must be taken that it is not seen simply as a procedure to be memorised and then applied in a routine manner to every new problem. Rather, it needs to be carefully developed over a range of different problems, highlighting the components that are developed with each new problem.

Analyse

- As pupils read a problem, the need to first read for the *meaning* of the problem can be stressed. This may require reading more than once and can be helped by asking pupils to state in their own words what the problem is asking them to do.

- Further reading will be needed to sort out which information is needed and whether some is not needed or if other information needs to be gathered from the problem's context (e.g. data presented within the illustration or table accompanying the problem), or whether the pupils' mathematical understandings need to be used to find other relationships among the information. As the form of the problems becomes more complex, this thinking will be extended to incorporate further ways of dealing with the information; for example, measurement units, fractions and larger numbers might need to be renamed to the same mathematical form.

- Thinking about any processes that might be needed and the order in which they are used, as well as the type of answer that could occur, should also be developed in the context of new levels of problem structure.

- Developing a capacity to see 'through' the problem's expression—or context to see similarities between new problems and others that might already have been met—is a critical way of building expertise in coming to terms with and solving problems.

Expanding the problem-solving process

A fuller model to manage problem-solving can gradually emerge:

- Put the solution back into the problem.
- Does the answer make sense?
- Does it solve the problem?
- Is it the only answer?
- Could there be another way?

- Read carefully.
- What is the problem asking?
- What is the meaning of the information? Is it all needed? Is there too little? Too much?
- Which operations will be needed and in what order?
- What sort of answer is likely?
- Have I seen a problem like this before?

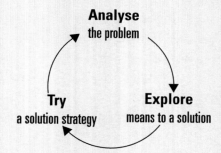

Analyse
the problem

Try
a solution strategy

Explore
means to a solution

- Use materials or a model.
- Use a calculator.
- Use pencil and paper.
- Look for a pattern.

- Use a diagram or materials.
- Work backwards or backtrack.
- Put the information into a table.
- Try and adjust.

Explore

- When a problem is being explored, some problems will require the use of materials to think through the whole of the problem's context. Others will demand the use of diagrams to show what is needed. Another will show how systematic analysis of the situation using a sequence of diagrams, on a list or table, is helpful. As these ways of thinking about the problem are understood, they can be included in the cycle of steps.

Try

- Many pupils often try to guess a result. This can even be encouraged by talking about 'guess and check' as a means to solve problems. Changing to 'try and adjust' is more helpful in building a way of thinking and can lead to a very powerful way of finding solutions.

- When materials, a diagram or table have been used, another means to a solution is to look for a pattern in the results. When these have revealed what is needed to try for a solution, it may also be reasonable to use pencil and paper or a calculator.

Analyse

- The point in the cycle where an answer is assessed for reasonableness (e.g. whether it provides a solution, is only one of several solutions or whether there may be another way to solve the problem) also needs to be brought to the fore as different problems are met.

The role of calculators

When calculators are used, pupils devote less time to basic calculations, providing time that might be needed to either explore a solution or find an answer to a problem. In this way, attention is shifted from computation, which the calculator can do, to thinking about the problem and its solution—work that the calculator cannot do. It also allows more problems (and more realistic problems) to be addressed in problem-solving sessions. In these situations, a calculator serves as a tool rather than a crutch, requiring pupils to think through the problem's solution in order to know how to use the calculator appropriately. It also underpins the need to make sense of the steps along the way and any answers that result, as keying incorrect numbers, operations or order of operations quickly leads to results that are not appropriate.

Choosing, adapting and extending problems

When problems are selected, they need to be examined to see if pupils already have an understanding of the underlying mathematics required and that the problem's expression can be meaningfully read by the group of pupils who will be attempting the solution—though not necessarily by *all* pupils in the group. The problem itself should be neither too easy (so that it is just an exercise, repeating something readily done before), nor too difficult (thus beyond the capabilities of most or all in the group), and engages the interests of the pupils. A problem should also be able to be solved in more than one way.

As a problem and its solution is reviewed, posing similar questions—where the numbers, shapes or measurements are changed—focuses attention back on what was entailed in analysing the problem and in exploring the means to a solution. Extending these processes to more complex situations enables the particular approach used to extend to other situations and shows how to analyse patterns to obtain more general methods or results. It also highlights the importance of a systematic approach when conceiving and discussing a solution and can lead to pupils asking themselves further questions about the situation, thus posing problems of their own as the significance of the problem's structure is uncovered.

Problem structure and expression

When analysing a problem it is also possible to discern critical aspects of the problem's form and relate this to an appropriate level of mathematics and problem expression when choosing or extending problems. A problem of first-level complexity uses simple mathematics and simple language. A 'second-level' may have simple language and more difficult mathematics or more difficult language and simple mathematics; while a third-level has yet more difficult

language and mathematics. Within a problem, the processes that need to be used may be more or less obvious, the information that is required for a solution may be too much or too little, and strategic thinking may be needed in order to come to terms with what the problem is asking.

Level	processes obvious	processes less obvious	too much information	too little information	strategic thinking
increasing difficulty with problem's expression and mathematics required	simple expression, simple mathematics				
	more complex expression, simple mathematics				
	simple expression, more complex mathematics				
	complex expression, complex mathematics				

The varying levels of problem structure and expression

(i) The processes to be used are relatively obvious as: these problems are comparatively straightforward and contain all the information necessary to find a solution.

(ii) The processes required are not immediately obvious as these problems contain all the information necessary to find a solution but demand further analysis to sort out what is wanted and pupils may need to reverse what initially seemed to be required.

(iii) The problem contains more information than is needed for a solution as these problems contain not only all the information needed to find a solution, but also additional information in the form of times, numbers, shapes or measurements.

(iv) Further information needs to be gathered and applied to the problem in order to obtain a solution. These problems do not contain first-hand all the necessary information required to find a solution but do contain a means to obtain the required information. The problem's setting, the pupil's mathematical understanding or the problem's wording need to be searched for the additional material.

(v) Strategic thinking is required to analyse the question in order to determine a solution strategy. Deeper analysis, often aided by the use of diagrams or tables, is needed to come to terms with what the problem is asking so as to determine a means to a solution.

This analysis of the nature of problems can also serve as a means of evaluating the provision of problems within a mathematics programme. In particular, it can lead to the development of a full range of problems, ensuring they are included across all problem forms, with the mathematics and expression suited to the level of the pupils.

Assessing problem-solving

Assessment of problem-solving requires careful and close observation of pupils working in a problem-solving setting. These observations can reveal the range of problem forms and the level of complexity in the expression and underlying mathematics that a pupil is able to confidently deal with. Further analysis of these observations can show to what extent the pupil is able to analyse the question, explore ways to a solution, select one or more methods to try and then analyse any results obtained. It is the combination of two fundamental aspects—the types of problem that can be solved and the manner in which solutions are carried out—that will give a measure of a pupil's developing problem solving abilities, rather than a one-off test in which some problems are solved and others are not.

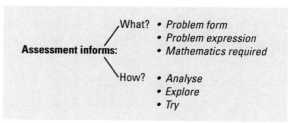

Observations based on this analysis have led to a categorisation of many of the possible difficulties that pupils experience with problem-solving as a whole, rather than the misconceptions they may have with particular problems.

These often involve inappropriate attempts at a solution based on little understanding of the problem.

Problem	Likely causes
Pupil is unable to make any attempt at a solution.	• lack of interest • feels overwhelmed • cannot think of how to start to answer question • needs to reconsider complexity of steps and information
Pupil has no means of linking the situation to the implicit mathematical meaning.	• needs to create diagram or use materials • needs to consider separate parts of question, then bring parts together
Pupil uses an inappropriate operation.	• misled by word cues or numbers • has underdeveloped concepts • uses rote procedures rather than real understanding
Pupil is unable to translate a problem into a more familiar process.	• cannot see interactions between operations • lack of understanding means he/she unable to reverse situations • data may need to be used in an order not evident in the problem statement or in an order contrary to that in which it is presented

A major cause of possible difficulties is the *lack of a well-developed plan* of attack, leading pupils to focus on the *surface level* of problems. In such cases, pupils:

- locate and manipulate numbers with little or no thought as to their relevance to the problem
- try a succession of different operations if the first ones attempted do not yield a (likely) result
- focus on keywords for an indication of what might be done without considering their significance within the problem as a whole
- read problems quickly and cursorily to locate the numbers to be used
- use the first available word cue to suggest the operation that might be needed.

Other possible difficulties result from a focus on being quick, which leads to:

- no attempt to assess the reasonableness of an answer
- little perseverance if an answer is not obtained using the first approach tried
- not being able to access strategies to which they have been introduced.

When the approaches to problem processing developed in this series are followed and the specific suggestions for solving particular problems or types of problems are discussed with pupils, these difficulties can be minimised, if not entirely avoided. Analysing the problem before starting leads to an understanding of the problem's meanings. The cycle of steps within the model means that nothing is tried before the intent of the problem is clear and the means to a solution have been considered. Focussing on a problem's meanings, and discussing what needs to be done, builds perseverance. Making sense of the steps that need to be followed and any answers that result are central to the problem-solving process that is developed. These difficulties are unlikely among those who have built up an understanding of this way of thinking.

A final comment

If an approach to problem-solving can be built up using the ideas developed here and the problems in the investigations on the pages that follow, pupils will develop a way of thinking about and with mathematics that will allow them to readily solve problems and generalise from what they already know to understand new mathematical ideas. They will engage with these emerging mathematical conceptions from their very beginnings, be prepared to debate and discuss their own ideas, and develop attitudes that will allow them to tackle new problems and topics. Mathematics can then be a subject that is readily engaged with, and become one in which the pupil feels in control, instead of one in which many rules devoid of meaning have to be memorised and (hopefully) applied at the right time and place. This enthusiasm for learning and the ability to think mathematically will then lead to a search for meaning in new situations and processes that will allow mathematical ideas to be used across a range of applications in school and everyday life.

A NOTE ON CALCULATOR USE

Many of the problems in this series demand the use of a number of consecutive calculations, often adding, subtracting, multiplying or dividing the same amount in order to complete entries in a table or see a pattern. This demands (or will build) a certain amount of sophisticated use of the memory and constant functions of a simple calculator.

1. To add a number such as 9 repeatedly, it is sufficient on most calculators to enter an initial number (e.g. 30) then press + 9 = = = = to add 9 over and over.

   - *30, 39, 48, 57, 66, ...*

   - *To add 9 to a range of numbers, enter the first number (e.g. 30) then press + 9 = 30 + 9 = 39, 7 = gives 16, 3 = gives 12, 21 = gives 30, ...*

   - *These are the answers when 9 is added to each number.*

2. To subtract a number such as 5 repeatedly, it is sufficient on most calculators to enter an initial number (e.g. 92) then press – 5 = = = = to subtract 5 over and over.

   - *92, 87, 82, 77, 72, ...*

   - *To subtract 5 from a range of numbers, enter the first number (e.g. 92) then press – 5 = 95 – 5 = 90, 68 = gives 63, 43 = gives 38, 72 = gives 67, ...*

   - *These are the answers when 5 is subtracted from each number.*

3. To multiply a number such as 10 repeatedly, most calculators now reverse the order in which the numbers are entered. Enter 10 x, then press an initial number (e.g. 15) = = = = to multiply by 10 over and over.

   - *10, 150, 1500, 15 000, 150 000, ...*

   - *This also allows squaring of numbers: 4 x = gives 16.*

   - *Continuing to press = gives more powers:*

   - *4 x = = gives 64, 4 x = = = gives 256; 4 x = = = = gives 1024 and so on.*

   - *To multiply a range of numbers by 10, enter 10 x then the first number (e.g. 90) and =*

   - *10 x 90 = 900, 45 = gives 450, 21 = gives 210, 162 = gives 1620, ...*

   - *These are the answers when each number is multiplied by 10.*

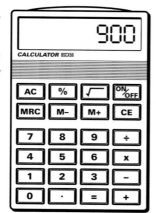

4. To divide by a number such as 4 repeatedly, enter a number (e.g. 128).

   - *Then press ÷ 4 = = = = to divide each result by 4.*

   - *32, 8 , 2, 0.5, ...*

   - *These are the answers when the given number is divided by 4.*

5. Using the memory keys M+, M– and MR will also simplify calculations. A result can be calculated and added to memory (M+). Then a second result can be calculated and added to (M+) or subtracted from (M–) the result in the memory. Pressing MR will display the result. Often this will need to be performed for several examples as they are entered onto a table or patterns are explored directly. Clearing the memory after each completed calculation is essential!

   A number of calculations may also need to be made before addition, subtraction, multiplication or division with a given number. That number can be placed in memory and used each time without needing to be re-keyed.

6. The % key can be used to find percentage increases and decreases directly.

   - *To increase or decrease a number by a certain per cent (e.g. 20%), simply key the number and press + 20% or – 20% to get the answer:*

   - *80 + 20% gives 96 (not 100) – 20% of 80 is 16, 80 + 16 is 96.*

   - *90 – 20% gives 72 (not 70) – 20% of 90 is 18, 90 – 18 is 72.*

7. While the square root key can be used directly, finding other roots is best done by a 'try and adjust' approach using the multiplication constant described above (in point 3).

Problem-solving in mathematics

Pupil worksheets and teachers notes

Problem-solving

To use spatial visualisation and logical reasoning to solve problems.

Curriculum links

England (Year 4)
- Using and applying: Identify and use patterns, relationships and properties of shapes.
- Using and applying: Report solutions to puzzles and problems.

Northern Ireland (Key Stage 2)
- Processes in maths: Develop a range of strategies for problem solving, looking for ways to overcome difficulties.
- Processes in maths: Recognise general patterns and relationships and make predictions about them.

Scotland (First and Second)
- Properties of 3-D objects: Explore a range of 3-D objects and where they are used in the environment (2nd).

Wales (Key Stage 2)
- Skills: Select and use the appropriate mathematics to solve problems in a variety of contexts.
- Skills: Recognise, and generalise in words, patterns that arise in spatial situations.

Materials:

Cubes such as wooden, Multilink™ or Unifix™ cubes.

Focus

These pages explore arrangements and dissections of three-dimensional shapes in order to determine how particular outcomes are formed. Spatial as well as logical thinking and organisation are involved as pupils investigate all likely arrangements to ensure that the final forms match the given criteria or visualise a given shape in terms of its component parts.

Discussion

Page 3

Pupils need to be able to visualise the arrangements of cubes, oranges and cans stacked in several layers.

Some will see the first drawing as consisting of one layer of 16 cubes, another of nine cubes, another of four cubes and then one cube on top. Others will see slices going down the staircase—10, then 9, 7 and 4—or see these building upwards.

They will need 30 cubes to build the arrangement. The different ways that the diagram can be visualised and the staircase built should be discussed with the class.

The stacks of oranges and cans use either a triangular base or square base and have the shapes stacked on the intersection of the ones below rather than one on top of another.

The final shape does not follow a simple pattern and pupils will need to visualise how the blocks are stacked and find a way to organise their count. This will influence the building of their own structures and how they visualise and keep track of the individual cubes.

Page 4

Seeing how cubes make a larger structure is now extended to include applying paint to a completed shape and visualising the effect on the individual cubes. Pupils may need to build the structures and manipulate blocks in order to see what happens. Some pupils may need to place labels on certain faces of the cube to help them come to terms with what the questions are asking.

Encourage the systematic analysis of the shapes when discussing the results: Could any cubes have all sides painted? Where would cubes with six, four, three, two or one side(s) painted be found? Which of these are possible and which are not possible on each shape?

Page 5

The problems on this page extend the thinking needed to visualise and see patterns. When the large cube was cut into smaller cubes, some of the smaller cubes would have been hidden inside the whole and careful analysis is needed to determine the way individual cubes would be painted. A table of possibilities is one way of keeping track of what happened.

Possible difficulties

- Unable to visualise the cubes in the representations on the two-dimensional page
- Only considers the cubes that can be readily seen on the outside of the shapes

Extension

- Have pupils make stacks using different arrangements of cubes and others work out how many were used.
- Use isometric paper to draw the stacks they make and have other pupils see how many cubes are used.
- Extend the problems by asking what would happen if more blocks had been used—if each arm of the 'T' had one, two or more additional cubes before painting. What if the large block had been cut into cubes with sides of one centimetre? What if the cube was cut into 64 or 125 smaller cubes?

STACKING SHAPES

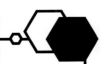

1. A set of steps was made by stacking one cube on top of another. How many cubes were needed to make the staircase?

_____

Find as many cubes as you think you need and make the staircase.

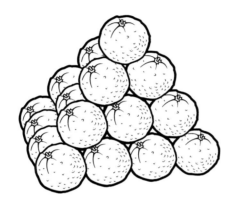

2. Greengrocers often stack fruit as a pyramid. How many oranges are in this stack?

_____

3. At the supermarket, you sometimes see cans of soup stacked for a display. How many cans are in this stack?

_____

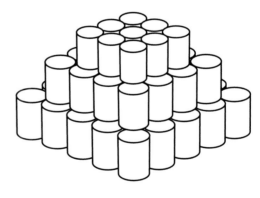

4. These cubes have been stacked one on top of another. Some of the cubes are hidden behind or beneath others and cannot be seen. How many cubes were used to build the shape?

_____

Get some cubes and build your own stack. Write the number of cubes you used and challenge a friend to work out how many you used without pulling your stack apart.

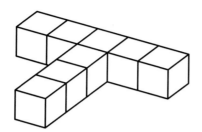

This shape was made using eight cubes. After they were joined together, the final shape was painted green on all of its sides. When it was taken apart again, some of the faces of the cubes have green paint and others do not.

1. How many of the individual cubes would have green paint on exactly four faces?

_____

2. Would any of the individual cubes have five faces painted? How many?

_____

3. Would any have three faces painted? How many?

_____

A wooden block is 8 cm long, 8 cm wide and 2 cm high. The block is painted blue on all six faces and then cut into 16 cubes, each with sides of 2 cm.

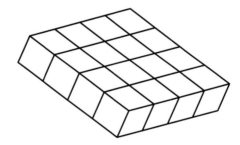

4. How many of the cubes would have blue paint on four faces?

_____

5. How many of the cubes would have only three faces painted?

_____

6. How many of the cubes would have only two faces painted?

_____

7. Why would there be no cubes with only one, five or six faces painted?

_____

_____

CUBE PAINTING

In the art gallery, a large polystyrene cube was hung from a string and spray-painted red on all six faces. It was then cut into twenty-seven smaller cubes to be used by children to make shapes of their own.

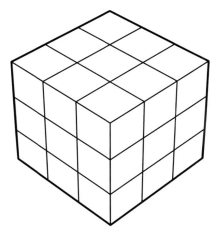

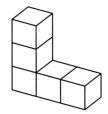  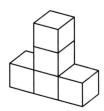

1. With the large cube cut, how many of the individual cubes would have red paint on only three faces?

   _____

2. Would any of the cubes have no red paint? _____

3. How many? _____

4. Describe the cubes.

Number of faces painted	Number of cubes
0	
1	
2	
3	
	Total =

5. When you count all of the cubes you have described, are all 27 included?

   _____

Problem-solving

To use strategic thinking to solve problems.

Curriculum links

England (Year 4)

- Using and applying: Solve one-step and two-step problems involving numbers and choose and carry out appropriate calculations.
- Using and applying: Identify and use patterns, relationships and properties of numbers.
- Using and applying: Report solutions to puzzles and problems.

Northern Ireland (Key Stage 2)

- Processes in maths: Develop a range of strategies for problem solving, looking for ways to overcome difficulties.
- Processes in maths: Recognise general patterns and relationships and make predictions about them.

Scotland (First and Second)

- Patterns and relationships: Explore number sequences (2nd).

Wales (Key Stage 2)

- Skills: Select and use the appropriate mathematics to solve problems in a variety of contexts.
- Skills: Recognise, and generalise in words, patterns that arise in spatial situations.

Materials

0–99 number board

0	1	2	3	4	5	6	7	8	9
10	11	12	13	14	15	16	17	18	19
20	21	22	23	24	25	26	27	28	29
30	31	32	33	34	35	36	37	38	39
40	41	42	43	44	45	46	47	48	49
50	51	52	53	54	55	56	57	58	59
60	61	62	63	64	65	66	67	68	69
70	71	72	73	74	75	76	77	78	79
80	81	82	83	84	85	86	87	88	89
90	91	92	93	94	95	96	97	98	99

Focus

This page explores pupils' understanding of the number system and their ability to solve questions about numbers. Pupils need to coordinate the reading and writing of numerals with the symbols involved in writing the numbers 400–600.

Discussion

Page 7

This problem explores pupils' ability to reason about the number system and keep track of the possibilities they find. Pupils need to discuss what it means to 'say' a number as opposed to 'writing' a digit.

When pronunciating certain numbers—for example, with numbers which include 'four'—it is important for pupils to include numbers which include the pronunciation of the word part 'four' within 'fourteen', 'forty', 'forty-one' etc.

If pupils take the problem further and try other number ranges, as suggested, they will find a different pattern altogether for the three hundreds as opposed to the four hundreds. After the five hundreds the patterns begin to repeat. When pupils notice this, they will have really come to terms with the strategic thinking needed to organise and solve problems with several interacting conditions.

Trying different number ranges or counting and writing in fives and 25s will provide different patterns as pupils coordinate what happens to the ones, tens and hundreds digits.

Possible difficulties

- Unable to keep track of the number of times they determine a digit or word
- Confusion between saying and writing the digits
- Not understanding that we say 'four' in numbers which contain 'forty', even though it is written differently to 'four' or 'fourteen'
- Thinking that 'five' is said for numbers with 'fifty'
- Confusion with 44, 55, etc. including only seeing the digit once when it actually occurs in both the ones and tens place

Extension

- Try other number ranges such as 300–500, 400–700 etc.
- Investigate the number of times 'five' is said and written when counting by fives or 25s.
- Make a table to display the results and present a description of the problems and their solution to another class.

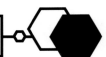

1. (a) How many times do you say 'four' when you count from four hundred to six hundred?

   _____

Four hundred, four hundred and one ...

   (b) How many times do you write '4' when you write all of the numbers from 400 to 600?

   _____

2. (a) If counting from four hundred to six hundred, would you say 'five' more or fewer times than you would say 'four'?

   _____

   (b) How many times would you say 'five'?

   _____

Four hundred and four, four hundred and five ...

   (c) How many times would your write '5' when writing all of the numbers from 400 to 600?

   _____

3. Try other 1-digit numbers. Can you see a pattern?

   _____

   _____

Problem-solving

To identify and use concepts about numeration.

Curriculum links

England (Year 4)
- Using and applying: Solve one-step and two-step problems involving numbers and choose and carry out appropriate calculations.
- Using and applying: Report solutions to puzzles and problems.
- Calculating: Add mentally two-digit whole numbers.

Northern Ireland (Key Stage 2)
- Processes in maths: Develop a range of strategies for problem solving, looking for ways to overcome difficulties.
- Number: Develop strategies to add mentally.

Scotland (First and Second)
- Addition: Use addition when solving problems (1st).

Wales (Key Stage 2)
- Skills: Select and use the appropriate mathematics to solve problems in a variety of contexts.
- Skills: Develop a variety of mental strategies of computation.
- Number: Use a variety of mental methods of computation.

Materials

counters, blocks or a calculator

Focus

These pages explore solving problems involving number sense, magic squares and logic. Pupils need to carefully analyse the problems to locate information necessary to find the magic number or the arrangement of numbers. Counters, blocks or a calculator can be used to assist as these problems focus on the concepts of number sense and number logic rather than basic facts.

Discussion

Page 9

This activity investigates possible combinations of numbers to make a total. Pupils have four scores which add together to make a total score and a list of numbers which make up the scores. Number 'sense' and the 'try and adjust' strategy are needed to find solutions.

For example, the score of 32, using the digits 5 and 9, requires the combination of 9, 9, 9 and 5; while a score of 57, using 24, 7 and 13 requires the combination of 24, 7, 13, 13.

Page 10

This investigation involves the concept of magic squares. Simple 3-by-3 magic squares have been used to establish the idea that each row, column and diagonal adds to the same magic number. In this case, the concept is further explored as pupils investigate a famous magic square.

The Dürer magic square has a number of points of interest aside from being a magic square. For example, not only does each row, column or diagonal add to the same number, so do the four corners, the four middle numbers and the four corner mini (2-by-2) grids. Also, it uses the numbers 1 to 16 and shows the year in which it was constructed.

Page 11

This page introduces pupils to the concept of sudoku. The word 'sudoku' roughly means 'digits must only occur once'. In this case a 4-by-4 grid has been used and every row, column and mini-grid must contain one of each of the numbers 1, 2, 3 and 4. More commonly a 9-by-9 grid is used, using the digits 1 to 9. No addition or basic facts are involved and pupils need to use logical reasoning to find solutions.

Possible difficulty

- Considering only rows or columns rather than rows, columns and diagonals in the magic squares or the smaller grids in the sudoku puzzles

Extension

- Investigate other magic squares and magic numbers.
- Explore sudoku games in magazines, newspapers and on the Internet that involve 4-by-4 grids as well as 9-by-9 grids.

STAR GAZE

 • • • • • • • • is a new computer game.
Each time you win, you collect stars.
Total the four stars to find your score.

1. Work out these scores.

(a)

Score: _____

(b)

Score: _____

(c)

Score: _____

2. Add combinations of the numbers given to find the score.

(a)

Score: 27

use only 3 and 8

(b)

Score: 32

use only 5 and 9

(c)

Score: 26

use only 6 and 7

(d)

Score: 16

use only 5, 2, 7

(e)

Score: 21

use only 8, 1, 4

(f)

Score: 28

use only 9, 5, 7

(g)

Score: 57

use only 24, 7, 13

(h)

Score: 71

use only 6, 19, 23

(i)

Score: 99

use only 23, 37, 16

MAGIC SQUARES

In magic squares, all of the numbers in each row, column and diagonal add to the same total.

7	0	5
2	4	6
3	8	1

1. This magic square has a magic number of _____.

Complete the magic squares below. Remember, all rows, columns and diagonals must add to the same total.

2. (a)

		11
	9	
7		3

3.

11		9
	8	
		5

Magic number: _____

Magic number: _____

(b) What do you notice about each number in the square?

_____

FAMOUS MAGIC SQUARES

16			13
5	10		8
9		7	
	15		1

The following magic square was constructed in 1514 by an artist named Albrecht Dürer. Complete the magic square and discover why it is so famous.

4. Magic number: _____

5. What do the four corners add to? _____

6. What do the four middle squares add to?

_____

7. What do the four squares in each corner add to?

_____

8. What digits have been used? _____

9. Can you see anything to do with the date it was first constructed?

_____

SUDOKU

Sudoku puzzles are made up of numbers and to solve them you must use logic to work out where the numbers go.

Every row, column and mini-grid must contain one of each of the numbers 1, 2, 3 and 4.

2	1	3	4

Row – has the numbers 1, 2, 3 and 4.

			4
			1
			2
			3

Column – has the numbers 1, 2, 3 and 4.

		3	4
		2	1

Mini-grid – has the numbers 1, 2, 3 and 4.

2	1	3	4
3	4	2	1
4	3	1	2
1	2	4	3

The completed sudoku has the numbers 1, 2, 3 and 4 in every row, column and mini-grid.

Complete each sudoku.

1.

1	2		3
	4	1	
	1	3	
4		2	1

2.

	1		2
		1	3
1	3		
4		3	

3.

	1	2	
	2	3	
	3	4	
	4	1	

4.

	1	2	
3		1	
	4		2
	3	4	

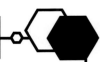

Problem-solving

To analyse and use information in word problems.

Curriculum links

England (Year 4)

- Using and applying: Solve one-step and two-step problems involving numbers and choose and carry out appropriate calculations.
- Using and applying: Report solutions to puzzles and problems.
- Calculating: Add or subtract mentally two-digit whole numbers.
- Calculating: Use efficient written methods to add and subtract two- and three-digit whole numbers.
- Calculating: Use written methods for multiplication.

Northern Ireland (Key Stage 2)

- Processes in maths: Develop a range of strategies for problem solving, looking for ways to overcome difficulties.
- Number: Develop strategies to add and subtract mentally.
- Number: Engage in a range of activities to develop understanding of the four operations of number, and use these operations to solve problems.

Scotland (First and Second)

- +/-/x/÷: Use addition, subtraction and multiplication when solving problems, making best use of the mental strategies and written skills developed (1st).
- +/-/x/÷: Determine which calculations are needed to solve problems involving whole numbers (2nd).

Wales (Key Stage 2)

- Skills: Select and use the appropriate mathematics to solve problems in a variety of contexts.
- Skills: Use effective methods of computation.
- Skills: Develop a variety of mental and written strategies of computation.
- Number: Use a veriety of mental methods of computation and extend written methods.
- Number: Recognise situations to which the four operations apply.

Materials

place value chart or a calculator

Focus

These pages explore word problems that mostly require addition or subtraction. Pupils need to determine what the problem is asking and, in many cases, calculate more than one step in order to find solutions. Analysis of the problems reveals that some questions contain additional information that is not needed.

If necessary, materials can be used to assist with the calculation as these problems are about reading for information and determining what the problem is asking rather than computation or basic facts.

Discussion

Page 13

These problems involve more than one step and may involve addition as well as subtraction. The wording has been kept simple to assist with the problem-solving process.

Pupils may choose a number of different ways to find a solution. For example, the second problem about people getting out (43) could be subtracted from the people going swimming (79) and then this number (36) could be added to 397 or, alternatively, 79 could be added to 397 and then 43 subtracted to obtain a solution. Pupils should be encouraged to explore and try different ways of arriving at a solution.

Page 14

This investigation relates to information about a lake with lily pads and frogs. The scenario begins with a certain number of frogs and lily pads. As new information is introduced, the numbers change to meet the new criteria; lily pads flower, grow and die while the frogs move from one lake to another.

Pupils are required to keep track of the new information and use it to answer the subsequent questions.

Page 15

A careful reading of each problem is needed to determine what the question is asking. In some cases, there is more information than needed and some problems contain numbers that are not needed to find a solution. Most problems require more than one step and both addition and subtraction are needed at times.

Again, there are a number of ways to find a solution and pupils should be encouraged to explore and try different possibilities of arriving at an answer. The last question involves pupils understanding that perch and carp are varieties of fish, while yabbies are crustaceans.

Possible difficulties

- Inability to identify the need to add, subtract or multiply
- Confusion over the need to carry out more than one step to arrive at a solution
- Using all the numbers listed in the problems rather than just the numbers needed

Extension

- Discuss how some problems can have more than one answer depending on different interpretations.
- Pupils could write their own problems and give them to others to solve.

THE WATER PARK

1. 361 adults and 173 children go through the gates before lunch, and 219 adults and 106 children enter after lunch. How many more adults than children are there?

_____

2. A total of 397 people are swimming in the six pools. Another 79 people go swimming while 43 people get out. How many people are now swimming in the pools?

_____

3. 248 people are lying on their towels. Later, 78 people go swimming, 26 people go for a walk and 36 people leave and get something to eat. How many people are still lying on their towels?

_____

4. In the water, 93 people are floating on swimming mats, 134 are swimming and 83 are wading in the shallow water. Soon, another 21 people with swimming mats arrive, but 14 also get out. How many people are now floating on swimming mats?

_____

5. At the cafeteria, 143 people are sitting eating lunch and 31 are standing in line waiting to order lunch. Two large tables of 12 finish their lunch and leave. How many people are now in the cafeteria?

_____

6. In the wave pool, 73 surfers are waiting to catch a wave. A large wave comes and 36 surfers catch and ride it to the beach. How many did not catch the wave?

_____

LILY PADS AND FROGS

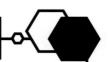

A lake has 279 lily pads and 372 frogs.

1. 87 of the lily pads are in flower. If each lily pad has three flowers, how many flowers are there altogether?

   _____

2. How many lily pads are not in flower? _____

3. Frogs like to sleep under the lily flowers. How many frogs cannot sleep under a flower?

   _____

4. When the rains come, 38 more lily pads burst into flower. How many lily pads are now in flower?

   _____

5. Are there now enough lily flowers for each frog to sleep under?

   _____

6. During spring, 129 new lily pads grow, 186 tadpoles turn into frogs and 75 lily pads die. How many lily pads are now in the lake?

   _____

7. During the summer, some frogs move to another lake. If 148 frogs move to another lake, how many stay behind?

   _____

GONE FISHING

1. On Saturday, 97 large yabbies, 21 small yabbies and 57 carp were caught. On Sunday, 126 large yabbies, 34 small yabbies and 83 carp were caught. How many yabbies were caught?

_____

2. During the week, 163 perch, 394 carp and 304 bass were caught in the dam. How much more bass than perch was caught?

_____

3. During a fishing competition, 923 perch were caught, tagged and then released back into the dam. 359 tagged perch were caught in October, 271 in November and 106 in December. How many tagged perch have not been caught?

_____

During the first weekend in June, 239 perch, 56 large yabbies, 17 small yabbies and 43 carp were caught. The next weekend, 161 perch, 79 large yabbies, 24 small yabbies and 65 carp were caught.

4. During which weekend were the most yabbies caught?

_____

5. During which weekend were the least amount of fish and yabbies caught?

_____

6. During which weekend were the most fish caught?

_____

Problem-solving

To solve problems involving money and make decisions based on particular criteria.

Curriculum links

England (Year 4)
- Using and applying: Solve one-step and two-step problems involving money and choose and carry out appropriate calculations.
- Using and applying: Report solutions to puzzles and problems.
- Counting and understanding number: Use decimal notation and relate to money.
- Calculating: Add and subtract £ and p.

Northern Ireland (Key Stage 2)
- Processes in maths: Develop a range of strategies for problem solving, looking for ways to overcome difficulties.
- Number: Use the four operations to solve problems involving money.

Scotland (First and Second)
- +/-/x/÷: Use addition, subtraction and multiplication when solving problems, making best use of the mental strategies and written skills developed (1st).
- +/-/x/÷: Explore problems involving decimals, and solve them using a variety of methods (2nd).
- Money: Use money to pay for items and work out change (1st).

Wales (Key Stage 2)
- Skills: Select and use the appropriate mathematics to solve problems in a variety of contexts.
- Skills: Use effective methods of computation.
- Skills: Develop a variety of mental and written strategies of computation.
- Money: Know and use the conventional way to record money.
- Money: Use the four operations to solve problems involving money.

Materials

counters, play money or a calculator

Focus

This page explores reading for information, obtaining information from another source (the takeaway menu) and using it to find solutions. The problems are about using money, making decisions based on money and comparing amounts of money, rather than adding or subtracting. Solutions can be obtained using materials and comparison of amounts. Counters, blocks, play money or a calculator can be used if needed.

Discussion

Page 17

Pupils read the items in the menu and note how much each costs. Pupils who are not familiar with money can still do the activity with a calculator. In most cases, pupils need to buy two or more of an item and then determine the amount spent and the change that remains.

The first two problems involve determining how much is spent on particular orders. Pupils need to take into consideration that more than one of some items have been ordered. The remaining problems analyse particular orders, with an additional focus on how much change would be received from £50.

Possible difficulties

- Unfamiliarity with the '£' symbol
- Not taking into account that they may need two or more of some items

Extension

- In pairs, pupils write their own questions based on the takeaway menu and give them to other pairs to solve.

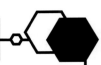

Chicken burger £4.50	Small chips £2.50
Chicken & cheese burger ... £5.00	Large chips £3.00
Chicken & bacon burger £5.50	Small drink £1.50
Chicken & chips £6.00	Large drink £2.50

How much money did the people spend at the takeaway shop?

1.
Liam ordered ...

1 chicken burger

1 large chips

1 small drink

Amount spent: ....

2.
Rosanna ordered ...

1 chicken & chips

2 chicken & bacon burgers

3 large drinks

Amount spent: ....

How much money did the following people spend and how much change did they receive from £50?

3.
Kayla ordered ...

2 chicken & bacon burgers
1 large chips
2 large drinks

Amount spent: ....

Change: ....

4.
Salam ordered ...

3 chicken & chips
2 chicken & cheese burgers
5 small drinks

Amount spent: ....

Change: ....

5.
Julian ordered ...

3 chicken burgers
3 large chips
3 large drinks

Amount spent: ....

Change: ....

6.
Danny ordered ...

2 chicken & bacon burgers
2 chicken & cheese burgers
4 large drinks

Amount spent: ....

Change: ....

7. Who spent the most? _____

Problem-solving

To use strategic thinking to solve problems.

Curriculum links

England (Year 4)

- Using and applying: Solve one-step and two-step problems involving numbers and measures, and choose and carry out appropriate calculations.
- Using and applying: Represent a puzzle or problem using number sentences or diagrams and use these to solve the problem.
- Using and applying: Report solutions to puzzles and problems.

Northern Ireland (Key Stage 2)

- Processes in maths: Develop a range of strategies for problem solving, looking for ways to overcome difficulties.
- Processes in maths: Interpret situations mathematically, using appropriate diagrams.
- Number: Develop an understanding of place value.
- Number: Use the four operations to solve problems.
- Measures: Use the four operations to solve measure problems.

Scotland (First and Second)

- Number processes: Explain the link between a digit, its place and its value (1st).
- +/-/x/÷: Determine which calculations are needed to solve problems involving whole numbers (2nd).

Wales (Key Stage 2)

- Skills: Select and use the appropriate mathematics to solve problems in a variety of contexts.
- Skills: Use effective methods of computation.
- Skills: Develop a variety of mental and written strategies of computation.
- Number: Understand place value in relation to the position of digits.
- Number: Use a variety of mental methods of computation and extend written methods.

Materials

counters in two different colours (1 of one colour, 17 of another colour)

Focus

These pages explore more complex problems in which the most difficult step is to find a way of coming to terms with the problem and what the question is asking. Using materials to explore the situation is one way in which this can be done. Another is to use a diagram to assist in thinking backwards or making trials and adjusting to find a solution that matches all of the conditions.

Discussion

Page 19

There are several ways these problems can be solved.

One way is to work backwards or 'backtrack' from the final position; for example: Lucy finishes in eighth position, must pass 11 cars, then be passed by five cars to get back to her original position. Counters can be used to model the process of cars passing and being passed. Using a counter of one colour to represent Lucy's car and counters of a second colour to represent the other 17 cars helps pupils keep track of who's passing who. Other pupils might prefer to base their solution on the diagram on the page to model what has happened.

Alternatively, pupils may choose a position for Lucy and work through each of the events in the race. If Lucy does not end up in eighth place, an adjustment can be made to determine the original starting position.

Page 20

These problems challenge pupils' understanding as they investigate the ways the digits can be placed according to set criteria. Some pupils will use the listed information in order to discard combinations until only the correct number remains, while other pupils may prefer to try each number in turn against all of the criteria until they find one number that answers all conditions. In each case, pupils need to take into consideration the information given about how large or small a number is.

Page 21

The puzzle scrolls contain a number of different problems, all of which require strategic thinking to find the solutions. In most cases, pupils will find tables, lists and diagrams helpful when exploring the different possibilities. Certain problems may have different answers, depending on the criteria the pupils use; for example, in the investigation about the length of rope the size of the ruler is not stated, so it may be necessary to consider both of the common ruler sizes of 30 cm and 1 m. The investigation about each combination of digits that total to 17 each can be rearranged to give six possibilities, giving 42 different numbers.

Possible difficulties

- Using only the 11 cars that Lucy passed to determine her starting position
- Not taking into consideration all the criteria for the serial numbers
- Considering only some aspects of the puzzle scrolls

Extension

- Pupils write their own car race problems based on the questions.
- Pupils could use a different context other than racing cars for their stories.
- Pupils write their own criteria for working out a serial number.
- Explore other shapes and how many triangles, squares or rectangles there are in them.

THE BIG RACE

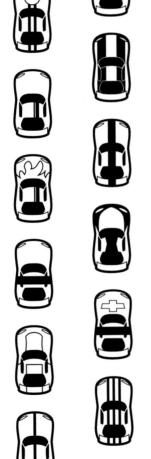

At the start of the race, the cars line up in their starting position.

1. Lucy is driving one of the 18 cars in the race. During the race she passes eleven cars before being passed by five cars. She finished eighth in the race.

   In what position did Lucy start the race?

   _____

2. Thao started in fifth place. During the race 10 cars passed him.

   How many cars does he need to pass to win the race?

   _____

3. Paula won the race. During the race four cars passed her and then she passed 12 cars.

   In what position did she start the race?

   _____

4. Luke is driving one of the 18 cars in the race. During the race he passes 10 cars before being passed by two cars. He finished third in the race.

   In what position did Luke start the race?

   _____

Prim-Ed Publishing®   www.prim-ed.com

Problem-solving in mathematics

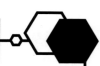

SERIAL NUMBERS

1. The serial number of my MP3 player is a four-digit number less than 6000 and has the digits 3, 4, 6 and 9.

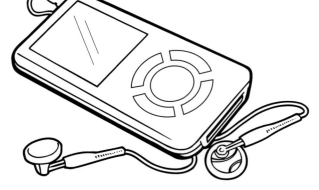

   The 4 is next to the 9.
   The 3 is not next to the 4.
   The 6 is not next to the 3.

   What is the serial number? _____

2. The serial number of my camera is a four-digit number more than 5000 and has the digits 5, 2, 7 and 3.

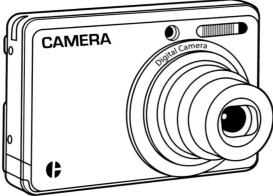

   The 2 is next to the 7.
   The 5 is not next to the 2.
   The 3 is not next to the 5.

   What is the serial number? _____

3. The serial number of my sister's MP3 player is a four-digit number less than 7000 and has the digits 2, 3, 5 and 8.

   The 3 is next to the 8.
   The 2 is not next to the 3.
   The 5 is not next to the 2.

   What is the serial number? _____

Problem-solving in mathematics   www.prim-ed.com   Prim-Ed Publishing®

1. Which two consecutive numbers add together to make 191? Can you find three consecutive numbers that add together to make 191? Explain your answer.

2. Cards measuring 20 cm by 30 cm were cut from a 2 m by 3 m sheet of cardboard.

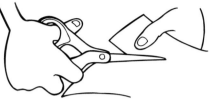

How many cards were cut?

3. How many triangles are in the shape below?

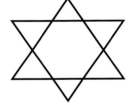

4. Margie bought her puppy on Thursday 19 July.

What days of the week were the first and last days of the month?

5. Robbie bought 60 m of rope but the ruler used to measure the rope was 1cm too long.

How much rope did he really get?

6. My house number has three digits that add to 17. My number could be 935.

What else could it be?

Problem-solving

To analyse and use information in word problems.

Curriculum links

England (Year 4)
- Using and applying: Solve one-step and two-step problems involving numbers and choose and carry out appropriate calculations.
- Using and applying: Report solutions to puzzles and problems.
- Calculating: Add or subtract mentally two-digit whole numbers.
- Calculating: Use efficient written methods to add and subtract two- and three-digit whole numbers.
- Calculating: Use written methods for multiplication.

Northern Ireland (Key Stage 2)
- Processes in maths: Develop a range of strategies for problem solving, looking for ways to overcome difficulties.
- Number: Develop strategies to add and subtract mentally.
- Number: Engage in a range of activities to develop understanding of the four operations of number, and use these operations to solve problems.

Scotland (First and Second)
- +/-/x/÷: Use addition, subtraction and multiplication when solving problems, making best use of the mental strategies and written skills developed (1st).
- +/-/x/÷: Determine which calculations are needed to solve problems involving whole numbers (2nd).

Wales (Key Stage 2)
- Skills: Select and use the appropriate mathematics to solve problems in a variety of contexts.
- Skills: Use effective methods of computation.
- Skills: Develop a variety of mental and written strategies of computation.
- Number: Use a variety of mental methods of computation and extend written methods.
- Number: Recognise situations to which the four operations apply.

Materials

Base 10 materials, place value chart, calculator

Focus

These pages explore word problems that require addition, subtraction or multiplication. The wording has been kept fairly simple to help with the problem-solving process. Pupils need to determine what the problem is asking and in many cases carry out more than one step in order to find solutions. Materials can be used to assist with the calculation if necessary as these problems are about reading for information and determining what the problem is asking rather than computation or basic facts.

Discussion

Page 23
These problems involve addition, subtraction and multiplication. In most cases more than one step is needed to find a solution. The wording has been kept fairly simple to assist with the problem-solving process. The last problem requires pupils to work backwards to find a solution: If Samantha needs 82 lilies and only orders an extra 47, then she would have had 35 left over on Friday. When the delivery is short by seven lilies, she will have 75 lilies rather than the 82 she needs.

Page 24
These investigations involve addition, subtraction and multiplication. Pupils may find it helpful to draw a diagram to work out what is happening in the story and to determine what needs to be multiplied to find a solution. The problems about selling the bunches of parsley in the morning and afternoon (questions 5 and 6) also involves information from Problem 4. This problem explores how many bunches of parsley Simon has not sold and is used in the next problem.

Page 25
The wording and the steps involved in these problems have been kept fairly simple to assist with the problem-solving process. Pupils may find it helpful to draw a picture in order to work out what is happening in each story. In most cases more than one step is needed to find a solution. Problem 2 contains information about white loaves and multi-grain loaves which is not needed to find a solution.

Possible difficulties
- Inability to identify the need to add, subtract or multiply
- Confusion over the need to carry out more than one step to arrive at a solution
- Using all the numbers listed in the problems rather than just the numbers needed

Extension
- Pupils could write their own problems and give them to other pupils to solve.

SAMANTHA'S FLOWER SHOP

1. Samantha has 38 pots of chrysanthemums left over from Friday. On Saturday, she receives a delivery of another 75 pots of chrysanthemums and sells 59 pots. How many pots of chrysanthemums does she have available to sell on Sunday?

2. (a) The delivery truck delivers 384 roses. 186 roses are sold in the morning. In the afternoon, she receives an order for 26 bunches of five roses. Does Samantha have enough roses for this order?

   (b) How many roses does she still have available to sell?

3. Samantha has 120 red roses and 100 yellow roses. She makes 14 bunches, using 9 roses in each bunch. Does she have enough roses to make another 8 bunches?

4. (a) Samantha has some lilies left at the end of the day on Friday. She has orders for 82 lilies for her customers on Saturday. She orders 47 lilies to make up the shortfall. How many lilies did she have left over on Friday?

   (b) When she goes to work on Saturday, she finds that only 40 lilies were delivered. How many lilies does she have for her orders?

HERB MARKET

1. Simon has a herb stall. He sold 373 bunches of fresh herbs and 218 pots of herb plants. How many more bunches of fresh herbs than pots were sold?

_____

2. Simon has six trays of herb pots. How many pots does he have if each tray holds 24 pots?

_____

3. Simon sells small bags of herb seeds. Each bag holds eight seeds. How many seeds does he need to make 45 bags?

_____

4. Simon has three boxes of parsley. Each box has 65 bunches of parsley. How many bunches of parsley can he sell?

_____

5. Simon sells 41 bunches of parsley in the morning and 48 bunches in the afternoon. How many bunches does he have left?

_____

6. The next day, he sells 54 bunches of parsley in the morning and 52 bunches in the afternoon. How many bunches does he have now?

_____

7. Simon has 8 boxes of herb plants delivered. Each box contains 12 plants. He unpacks 3 boxes in the morning and 2 boxes in the afternoon. How many plants has he unpacked?

_____

Problem-solving in mathematics   www.prim-ed.com   Prim-Ed Publishing®

AT THE BAKERY

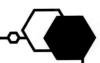

1. The baker baked 624 Christmas cakes. She took orders for 287 cakes on Monday, 265 cakes on Tuesday and 298 cakes on Wednesday. How many more Christmas cakes does she need to make?

2. On Saturday, 83 white loaves, 147 wholemeal loaves and 163 multi-grain loaves were sold. On Sunday, 132 white loaves, 169 wholemeal loaves and 178 multi-grain loaves were sold. How many wholemeal loaves were sold over the weekend?

3. (a) The bakery bakes 15 trays of pies. Each tray holds 12 pies. How many pies does the bakery have available to sell?

   (b) If the bakery sells 83 pies, how many pies were not sold?

4. The bakery has 14 trays of fairy cakes. Each tray has 16 fairy cakes. It sold 23 fairy cakes during the first hour, 84 fairy cakes during the second hour and 73 fairy cakes during the third hour. How many fairy cakes can it sell for the rest of the day?

Problem-solving

To use patterns and logical reasoning to determine numbers in a table.

Curriculum links

England (Year 4)
- Using and applying: Solve one-step and two-step problems involving numbers and choose and carry out appropriate calculations.
- Using and applying: Identify and use patterns of numbers.
- Using and applying: Report solutions to puzzles and problems.

Northern Ireland (Key Stage 2)
- Processes in maths: Develop a range of strategies for problem solving, looking for ways to overcome difficulties.
- Processes in maths: Recognise general patterns and make predictions about them.
- Number: Explore and predict patterns of whole numbers.

Scotland (First and Second)
- Patterns and relationships: Explore number patterns (1st and 2nd).

Wales (Key Stage 2)
- Skills: Select and use the appropriate mathematics to solve problems in a variety of contexts.
- Skills: Recognise, and generalise in words, patterns that arise in numerical situations.
- Skills: Investigate and generalise repeating patterns and relationships.

Materials

calculator

Focus

This page explores ordering of numbers to discern patterns that allow larger numbers to be determined without laboriously writing or counting all of the numbers up to the point asked for. It also highlights the value of using factors and multiples when thinking about numbers.

Discussion

Page 27

With questions 1–4, most pupils will observe that any number with a 5 in the ones place occurs in Column E. However, they may be surprised that a number with a 0 in the ones place does not also occur in this column. Both 87 and 34 are placed in Column D—this may lead them to observe how each column contains two different types of numbers. Any number with 2 in the ones place occurs in Column B, so this is where 92 is; meanwhile, any number with 8 in the ones place, including 108, is in Column C.

The pattern is:

Digit in ones place	Column
1 or 0	A
2 or 9	B
3 or 8	C
4 or 7	D
5 or 6	E

The challenge now is to describe the row where each of the numbers occur! One pattern is that since the numbers occur in blocks of ten, then:

Digit in tens place	Column
0	1 and 2
1	2, 3 and 4
2	4, 5 and 6
3	6, 7 and 8
4	8, 9 and 10
5	10, 11 and 12
etc.	etc.

Some pupils may be able to describe this: Multiply the digit in the tens place by 2 to get the row with 0 in the ones place. The next row has the numbers with 1, 2, 3, 4 or 5 in the ones place; the one after for the numbers with 6, 7, 8 or 9 in the ones place ...

For example, a number with 10 tens must be in row 20, 21 or 22—108 will be in row 22.

For Question 5, the patterns for the ones digit is:

Digit in ones place	Column
1 or 6	A
5 or 0	B
2 or 7	C
4 or 9	D
3 or 8	E

Numbers with   0 tens are in rows 1–3
                     1 ten are in rows 4–8 etc.

With Question 6, comparing the two arrangements shows that only the digits 4 and 1 remain in the same columns. Some pupils may be able to observe that 20% of the numbers are unchanged.

Possible difficulties

- Thinking that writing out all of the numbers is the only way to be sure of a solution
- Only considering the ones place when searching for a pattern
- Unable to verbalise a mathematical description of how the numbers are placed

Extension

- Describe a pattern for the row where a number occurs in the second arrangement.

NUMBERS IN COLUMNS

The counting numbers are arranged in five columns: A, B, C, D and E.

1. In which column will 75 appear?

   _____

A	B	C	D	E
1	2	3	4	5
10	9	8	7	6
11	12	13	14	15
		...	17	16

2. In which column will you find:

   (a) 34? _____

   (b) 61? _____

   (c) 87? _____

   (d) 92? _____

   (e) 108? _____

3. In which row will you find:

   (a) 34? _____

   (b) 61? _____

   (c) 87? _____

   (d) 92? _____

   (e) 108? _____

4. Can you find and describe a pattern for the rows and columns to help you find where any number would be?

   _____

   _____

   _____

The arrangement of counting numbers was changed to:

A	B	C	D	E
1		2		3
	5		4	
6		7		8
	10		9	
11		...		

5. Can you describe a pattern for the columns to help you find numbers in this arrangement?

   _____

   _____

   _____

6. Do any numbers appear in the same column as they were in the first table?

   _____

   _____

   _____

Problem-solving

To read, interpret and analyse information.

Curriculum links

England (Year 4)

- Using and applying: Solve one-step and two-step problems involving numbers, and choose and carry out appropriate calculations.
- Using and applying: Report solutions to puzzles and problems.

Northern Ireland (Key Stage 2)

- Processes in maths: Develop a range of strategies for problem solving, looking for ways to overcome difficulties.
- Number: Develop an understanding of place value.

Scotland (First and Second)

- Number processes: Explain the link between a digit, its place and its value (1st).

Wales (Key Stage 2)

- Skills: Select and use the appropriate mathematics to solve problems in a variety of contexts.
- Number: Understand place value in relation to the position of digits.

Materials

calculator, number expander

Focus

These pages explore concepts of place value and number sense. The relationships among numbers and place value are analysed and pupils are encouraged to not only find numbers that are possible but also to disregard numbers that are not possible. Place value and number sense are needed rather than addition or multiplication.

Discussion

Page 29

These problems involve a list of information about numbers which pupils need to read, interpret and enter into a calculator to find a given number. An understanding of place value is needed to enter the information. Pupils may use a number expander to assist them with the place value if needed. No formal addition or subtraction is needed. With Question 1, pupils need to start with a number 100 less than 4086. Using an understanding of place value we know that the number has 40 hundreds and 1 hundred less would be 39 hundreds, so the starting number is 3986.

Page 30

These problems require pupils to think in terms of place value. As 10 cones fit into one box and 10 boxes fit into one carton an understanding of place value can be used to solve each problem. For example, Question 1 involves 9 boxes and 24 cartons. It can be solved by thinking in tens or by thinking in tens and hundreds. By understanding place value, it is known that there will be 90 cones in the boxes and 2400 cones in the cartons, giving a total of 2490 cones. No formal multiplication or addition is required. A number expander can be used to assist.

Page 31

In this investigation, pupils need to read and interpret the information and use it to find combinations that match specific criteria. Pupils need to think of possible combinations as well as discarding combinations that don't work.

With the first problem, each person should receive nine chocolate frogs. The combinations are eight and one, seven and two, six and three and five and four. Some problems involve a number of possible combinations. The second problem has three different possible combinations, while the last problem has many different combinations. The two children can be given anywhere from 6 to 21 chocolate frogs each and many totals have several possible combinations. However, since the question asks for a total of 12 frogs, the boxes could be 138 and 246 or 237 and 156.

Possible difficulties

- Poor understanding of place value
- Wanting to add, subtract or multiply rather than using place value or number sense
- Not considering all of the criteria

Extension

- Pupils could write other problems involving the ice-cream cones.
- Pupils could think up their own calculator problems and write the criteria to match.
- Work out the different possibilities for two children to have three boxes, each with totals of 11, 13, 14, 15, 16 and 17.

CALCULATOR PROBLEMS

Solve the problems. Use your calculator to help you.

1. Enter the number one hundred less than 4086. Take away 317 and add 2006. What number am I?

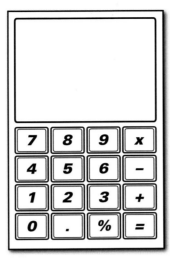

2. Enter the number with 562 tens and 9 ones. Add 23 hundreds, 4 tens and 7 ones. Take away 10 hundreds. What number am I?

3. Enter the number 1000 before 8293. Take away 24 tens. Add 3 ones and 634 tens. What number am I?

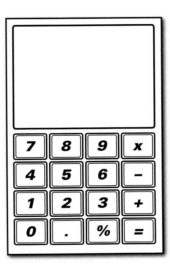

4. Enter the number 100 more than 6958. Make it 1000 more. Make it 100 less. Add 17 hundreds. What number am I?

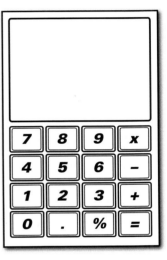

5. Enter the number with 82 hundreds and 5 ones. Add 34 tens. Take away 8 hundred and six. What number am I?

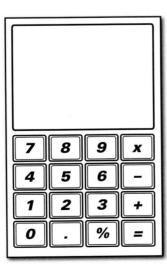

6. Enter the number one before 9900. Take away 89 tens. Make it 100 more. Take away 3 thousand and fourteen. What number am I?

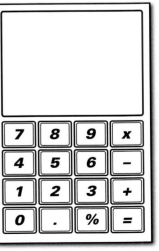

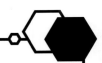

Prim-Ed Publishing®   www.prim-ed.com   Problem-solving in mathematics

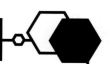

ICE-CREAM CONES

There are 10 ice-cream
cones in a box.

There are 10 boxes in
a carton.

Use the information above to solve these problems.

1. Anna has 9 boxes and 24 cartons of ice-
   cream cones. How many cones does she
   have?

   _____

2. The ice-cream factory has 593 boxes and
   70 loose cones still to be boxed. How
   many cartons will they need?

   _____

3. The truck delivered 48 cartons and
   17 boxes of ice-cream cones to the
   tuckshop. How many cones were
   delivered?

   _____

4. The truck has a load of 94 cartons and
   713 boxes of cones. It delivers 5600
   cones. How many cones does it have
   left?

   _____

5. The ice-cream shop has 52 boxes and 17 cartons of cones. It receives a
   delivery of 600 cones. How many cones does it now have?

   _____

6. At the end of the day, the ice-cream shop has 840 cones. If there are 6
   full cartons, how many extra boxes does it have?

   _____

www.prim-ed.com   Prim-Ed Publishing®

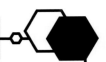

CHOCOLATE FROGS

Trudy is having a party. She has wrapped chocolate frogs in eight boxes. The first box has one chocolate frog, the second box has two chocolate frogs, the third box has three chocolate frogs and so on.

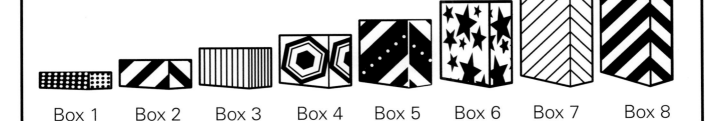

Box 1   Box 2   Box 3   Box 4   Box 5   Box 6   Box 7   Box 8

1. How many chocolates frogs has Trudy wrapped? _____

Trudy wants to give the same number of chocolates frogs to each person.

2. If she gives four children 2 boxes each, which boxes could she give to each person?

(a)    (b)    (c)   (d)

_____   _____   _____   _____

3. If she gives two children 4 boxes each, which boxes can she give?

(a)    (b)

_____   _____

4. If she gives two children 3 boxes each, which boxes could she give so each gets 12 chocolate frogs?

(a)    (b)

_____   _____

Prim-Ed Publishing®   www.prim-ed.com

Problem-solving in mathematics

Problem-solving

To interpret and organise information found in a series of interrelated statements and to use logical thinking to find solutions.

Curriculum links

England (Year 4)
- Using and applying: Solve one-step and two-step problems involving numbers, money and measures and choose and carry out appropriate calculations.
- Using and applying: Report solutions to puzzles and problems.
- Counting and understanding number: Use decimal notation for money and measurement.
- Calculating: Use efficient written methods to add and subtract two- and three-digit whole numbers.
- Calculating: Use written methods for multiplication.
- Calculating: Use a calculator to carry out one-step and two-step calculations involving all four operations.

Northern Ireland (Key Stage 2)
- Processes in maths: Develop a range of strategies for problem solving, looking for ways to overcome difficulties.
- Number: Engage in a range of activities to develop understanding of the four operations of number, and use these operations to solve problems.
- Number: Use the four operations to solve problems involving money.
- Measures: Use the four operations to solve measures problems.

Scotland (First and Second)
- +/-/x: Use addition, subtraction and multiplication when solving problems, making best use of the mental strategies and written skills developed (1st).
- +/-/x: Determine which calculations are needed to solve problems involving whole numbers (2nd).
- +/-/x: Solve problems involving decimals using a variety of methods (2nd).
- Measurement: Carry out calculations when solving measurement problems (2nd).

Wales (Key Stage 2)
- Skills: Select and use the appropriate mathematics to solve problems in a variety of contexts.
- Skills: Use effective methods of computation.
- Skills: Develop a variety of mental and written strategies of computation.
- Number: Use a variety of mental methods of computation and extend written methods.
- Number: Recognise situations to which the four operations apply.
- Measures and money: Use the four operations to solve problems involving money.

Materials

calculator

Focus

These pages explore interrelated statements within a problem situation using concepts of averages, distance and payments. Pupils need to read the stories carefully in order to take into consideration a number of different criteria. Tables and lists can be used to help manage the various criteria.

Discussion

Page 33

Each problem requires pupils to consider the information provided in a series of interrelated statements, all of which needs to be taken into consideration in order to find a solution. The use of a table or list may be very helpful to manage the data. For example, in the first problem, a table listing the various years can be used as a starting point. The problem states how many visitors came in 2003 and this information can be used to work out the number of visitors in 2007 (twice as many), and in turn this can be used to work out the numbers for 2006.

A similar table or list can be used for the other problems. The last problem contains additional information about the number of caves and the most visited caves, none of which is needed to find a solution.

Page 34

These problems explore the concept of average distance travelled over a period of time. In many cases the solution is not necessarily exact but rather an approximate time or distance; for example, Problem 2 states that Susie swims 100 m in 'about 2 minutes'. This is not an exact time and would vary from lap to lap, so the solution of how far she has swum would again be an approximate distance.

Problem 4 deals with the concept of distance travelled over a month. Discussion could centre around how this would vary from month to month. A table could be constructed to show the distance Brian runs during each month of the year. Some pupils may reason that he runs 156 km per week and that it takes a little less than four and a half weeks per month to travel around 700 kms. As an extra dimension, Problem 5 contains additional information about lunch as well as stopping and starting times which is not needed to find a solution.

Page 35

Each problem needs to be read carefully to determine what is being asked. In the first question, it is necessary to work out how many towels were purchased (four) in order to determine that eight are bought the next day (twice as many).

Problems 2 and 5 present two different ways of payment and both options need to be analysed to work out which option is best. Again, a table showing both options can be used to assist with the problem-solving process.

Possible difficulties

- Not using a table or list to manage the data
- Not understanding the term 'average'
- Confusion when dealing with approximate times and distances

Extension

- Construct a table to show the running distance and how it varies from month to month.

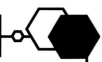

1. A large number of tourists visited Uluru during 2007. There were twice as many visitors in 2007 than in 2003. There were 6530 more visitors in 2007 than in 2006.

   If there were 298 460 visitors in 2003, how many were there in 2006?

   _____

2. During September, 258 000 tourists visited the Great Barrier Reef. April had twice as many visitors as January, but 4000 less than August. August had 8000 more visitors than September.

   How many visitors were there in January?

   _____

3. The Jenolan Caves Touring Company, in the Blue Mountains, currently offers tours to 11 different caves. Many of the visitors tour the Lucas, River and Chiefly caves. Due to storms, May was a poor month for visitors and only 19 970 people visited. June had 6230 more tourists than July and July had 3150 more than March. March had 4020 more visitors than May.

   How many visitors were there in June?

   _____

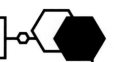

1. Erin caught a bus from London to Aberdeen. The bus left at 4 pm and, due to traffic, averaged 52 km for the first 2 hours. Once on the motorway, the bus averaged 96 km per hour for the next 6 hours.

    How far had Erin travelled? _____

2. Susie swims each morning in a 50 m pool. She can swim 100 m in about 2 minutes. She usually swims for an hour, has a short break and then swims for another hour.

    Approximately how far does she swim?

    _____

3. The train from Edinburgh to Penzance travels at an average speed of 105 km per hour. If Penzance is about 655 km from Edinburgh, how long will it take for the train to arrive?

    _____

4. Brian trains each day for the marathon. During the week he runs 8 km in the morning and 12 km in the afternoon. On the weekend he runs 28 km each day.

    How far does he run over a month?

    _____

5. Kim-Ly drove from Glasgow to London. She left at 9 am and averaged a speed of 94 km for 3 hours. She stopped for lunch and started again at 1pm. She drove for four hours and averaged 92 km per hour.

    How far had she travelled?

    _____

HOW MUCH?

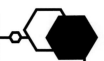

1. Derek paid £32 for towels that cost £8 each. The next day he saw the same towels for £6 each, so he bought twice as many as the day before. How much did he spend on towels?

2. Michael delivered 652 newspapers in seven hours. He can be paid by the number of newspapers he delivers or by the hour. The rate per newspaper is 5.5p and the hourly rate is £4.25 for the first hour and £3.50 for each other hour. Which option pays more money?

3. Alison bought apples from the market at a price of 6 apples for £2. She then sold them at her fruit shop at a price of 4 for £2 and made a profit of £10. How many apples did she sell?

4. The hardware shop sells shelf brackets both with and without screws. The brackets with screws cost £9.90 each and the ones without screws cost £6.50 each. Screws cost 80p each. If four screws are needed for each bracket, which is the cheapest option and by how much?

5. Wendy can be paid either by the day or by the number of trees she plants. She gets £1.20 per tree or £34.70 per day on weekdays and £48 per day on weekends. On average, she can plant about 37 trees per day. If she works Sunday to Sunday, which is the best payment option?

Problem-solving

To solve problems involving time and make decisions based on particular criteria.

Curriculum links

England (Year 4)

- Using and applying: Solve one-step and two-step problems involving numbers or measures and choose and carry out appropriate calculations.
- Using and applying: Report solutions to puzzles and problems.
- Calculating: Add mentally two-digit whole numbers.
- Measuring: Calculate time intervals from timetables.

Northern Ireland (Key Stage 2)

- Processes in maths: Develop a range of strategies for problem solving, looking for ways to overcome difficulties.
- Measures: Use timetables.

Scotland (First and Second)

- Time: Use timetables and schedules to plan events and activities, and make time calculations as part of planning (2nd).

Wales (Key Stage 2)

- Skills: Select and use the appropriate mathematics to solve problems in a variety of contexts.
- Measures and money: Use timetables.

Materials

Conversion table from 12-hour to 24-hour times, clock

Focus

This page explores reading for information, obtaining information from a number of sources (information about the plane, the timetable and the shuttle bus) and using it to find solutions. The problems involve thinking about and working with time. Decisions are about being 'too early' or 'too late' rather than an exact time.

Discussion

Page 37

Pupils read the information on the page and use it to find a number of solutions. Pupils who are not familiar with 24-hour time can still complete the activity by using a conversion table. The investigation can be used to introduce the concept of 24-hour time. Pupils need to read for information by using a number of sources and compare it against set criteria.

There are a number of flights that fit the criteria, with other flights arriving at Barcelona either 'too early' or 'too late'. Once some flights are deemed to be too late, they can be automatically excluded; for example, if the Star Airlines plane at 1700 would not arrive at Barcelona in time for dinner, then the flights at 1730 and 1800 can also be ruled out.

Similar thinking can be used for the flights that are too early; for example, catching the Star Airlines plane at 0830 would get to you to the hotel at around 1100, which is three hours too early. As such, the flights at 0900 and 1015 are also too early and can be automatically excluded.

Pupils need to think in terms of 24-hour time for the flight information; however, the before and after times of 2 pm and 6.30 pm are in 12-hour time. Pupils need to take into consideration that 2 pm and 6.30 pm are also 1400 and 1830 respectively.

The information regarding the waiting time at the airport is not needed. Some pupils may try to include this in their calculations.

Possible difficulties

- Unfamiliarity with a timetable
- Confusion with 24-hour time
- Thinking that an exact flight is needed rather than flights that fit within the time frame

Extension

- Use the information and timetable with other criteria; for example: If you need to be in Barcelona for a lunchtime meeting, what flights can you take?

SPANISH HOLIDAY

Imagine you have decided to travel to Barcelona for a holiday.

Look at the following information and plan your holiday. As most hotels and resorts have a 2 pm check-in time, you want to arrive after 2 pm but before dinner at 6.30 pm.

Plane information

• Wait time at airport: 1 hour
• Flight time to Barcelona: 2 hours

Star Airlines

Departure times	Flight numbers					
	ST23	ST32	ST47	ST51	ST68	ST74
	8:30	10:15	12:30	13:50	15:00	17:00

Lion Airlines

Departure times	Flight numbers					
	LA231	LA321	LA471	LA511	LA681	LA741
	9:00	11:45	14:30	15:30	17:30	18:00

Bus information

• Shuttle bus leaves airport: every 15 mins
• Travel time to hotel: 15 mins

1. I can catch the following flights: _____

2. These flights are too early: _____

3. These flights are too late: _____

Problem-solving

To use spatial visualisation and measurement to solve problems.

Curriculum links

England (Year 4)

- Using and applying: Solve one-step and two-step problems involving numbers and choose and carry out appropriate calculations.
- Using and applying: Represent a puzzle or problem using diagrams.
- Using and applying: Report solutions to puzzles and problems.
- Measuring: Measure and calculate perimeters.

Northern Ireland (Key Stage 2)

- Processes in maths: Develop a range of strategies for problem solving, looking for ways to overcome difficulties.
- Processes in maths: Interpret situations mathematically, using appropriate diagrams.
- Measures: Calculate perimeter.

Scotland (First and Second)

- Measurement: Find the perimeters of 2-D shapes (2nd).

Wales (Key Stage 2)

- Skills: Select and use the appropriate mathematics to solve problems in a variety of contexts.
- Measures and money: Find perimeters.

Materials

Paper to make and fold squares and equilateral triangles, triangle and square grid paper

Focus

These pages explore ideas of perimeter by using knowledge of squares and equilateral triangles to visualise shapes and to determine the lengths of sides within or composed of the shapes. Spatial and logical thinking, as well as numerical reasoning and organisation, are involved as pupils investigate the relationships among the shapes to determine the required distances.

Discussion

Page 39

Pupils need to be able to understand that the perimeter of the first shape (made from five squares) consists of 12 sides. This can be done by counting all of the sides in a systematic way or by seeing the shape made up of symmetric parts—two sections with five sides on the top and bottom and two in the middle, for example. Since the perimeter is 36 cm, the side of each small square must be 3 cm long. It may need to be explained to pupils that the shape is not to scale.

This reasoning is then applied to the other shapes with the number of sides multiplied by 3 cm. For questions 2

and 3, there are several possible shapes that can be made with a perimeter of 48 cm. The only criterion is that each perimeter must use 16 sides of the smaller squares; for example, a 3-by-5 rectangle or a 4-by-4 square:

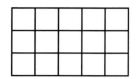 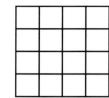

Page 40

Pupils need to be able to visualise the way in which the squares or triangle are folded and how the perimeter of the final shape would relate to the whole shape if unfolded. Pupils may need to use paper cut into squares:

Folding the square in Problem 1 in half and then half again shows 4 small squares when unfolded.

Each triangle contains 4 smaller triangles.

The perimeter of the triangle, 18 cm, is the same as 6 sides of the small triangle, so the side of the small triangle is 3 cm.

Page 41

This page continues the pupils' investigation of perimeters. While the first problem can be solved by thinking of the rectangle as being made up of two whole (6 cm) sides and two half (3 cm) sides, this does not readily generalise to the other ways the square is partitioned. Thinking of it as four half-sides allows the next shapes to be seen as, respectively, six third-sides and eight quarter-sides to readily solve the perimeter of each of the original squares. Another way to visualise solutions is to divide the squares and rectangles into smaller squares and see the results directly, as on the preceding pages.

Possible difficulties

- Uncertain of definition of perimeter
- Does not understand that the sides in a square or equilateral triangle are of equal length
- Unable to visualise the sides of the smaller shapes within the large shapes
- Cannot keep track of the number of sides that need to be used

Extension

- Have pupils investigate shapes made from small equilateral triangles in the same way as those made from small squares.
- Ask pupils to create their own examples of perimeters in squares where the square is folded into 5, 6 or more rectangles.

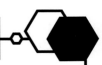

SQUARES AND PERIMETERS

Perimeter is the distance around the boundary of a shape.

Small squares, all of the same size, have been used to make these shapes.

Shape A

1. Shape A has a perimeter of 36 cm, what is the perimeter of each of these shapes?

   (a)

   _____

   (b)

   _____

   (c)

   _____

   (d)

   _____

   (e)

   _____

   (f)

   _____

   (g)

   _____

2. Can you draw a shape with a perimeter of 48 cm?

3. How many different shapes with a perimeter of 48 cm can you make? Draw them.

MORE PERIMETERS

ABCD is a square sheet of paper with a perimeter of 16 cm.

Imagine that you fold the paper so that corner A folds onto corner D and corner B folds onto corner C.

Now imagine that you fold it again so that A folds onto C.

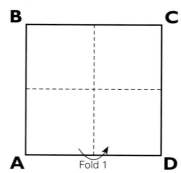

1. (a) After folding, what new shape would be created?

   _____

   (b) How long would its perimeter be? _____

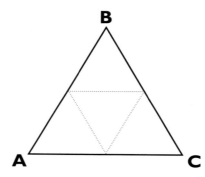

ABC is a triangle.

2. If it were folded along the dotted lines as shown, what would the new shape be?

   _____

The perimeter of the new shape is 9 cm.

3. What would the perimeter of the original triangle (ABC) have been?

   _____

4. When a larger square is folded in the same way as square ABCD, the resulting shape has a perimeter of 24 cm. What is the perimeter of the original square?

   _____

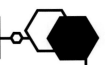

PERIMETERS IN SQUARES

Perimeter is the distance around the boundary of a shape.

1. A small sheet of paper has been folded in half and then cut along the fold to make two rectangles.

   The perimeter of each rectangle is 18 cm.

   What was the perimeter of the original square sheet of paper?

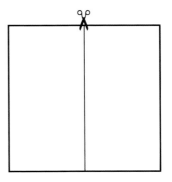

_____

2. A larger sheet of paper has been folded into thirds and then cut along each fold to make three rectangles.

   The perimeter of each rectangle is 48 cm.

   What was the perimeter of the original square sheet of paper?

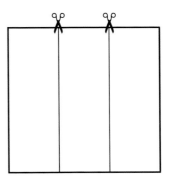

_____

3. A large square of plastic has been folded into quarters and then cut along each fold to make four rectangles.

   The perimeter of each rectangle is 50 m.

   What was the perimeter of the original square of plastic?

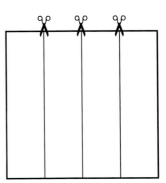

_____

Problem-solving

To analyse and use information in word problems.

Curriculum links

England (Year 4)

- Using and applying: Solve one-step and two-step problems involving numbers and choose and carry out appropriate calculations.
- Using and applying: Report solutions to puzzles and problems.
- Calculating: Add or subtract mentally two-digit whole numbers.
- Calculating: Use efficient written methods to add and subtract two- and three-digit whole numbers.
- Calculating: Use written methods for multiplication.

Northern Ireland (Key Stage 2)

- Processes in maths: Develop a range of strategies for problem solving, looking for ways to overcome difficulties.
- Number: Develop an understanding of place value.
- Number: Develop strategies to add and subtract mentally.
- Number: Engage in a range of activities to develop understanding of the four operations of number, and use these operations to solve problems.

Scotland (First and Second)

- Number processes: Explain the link between a digit, its place and its value (1st).
- +/-/x: Use addition, subtraction and multiplication when solving problems, making best use of the mental strategies and written skills developed (1st).
- +/-/x: Determine which calculations are needed to solve problems involving whole numbers (2nd).

Wales (Key Stage 2)

- Skills: Select and use the appropriate mathematics to solve problems in a variety of contexts.
- Skills: Use effective methods of computation.
- Skills: Develop a variety of mental and written strategies of computation.
- Number: Understand place value in relation to the position of digits.
- Number: Use a variety of mental methods of computation and extend written methods.
- Number: Recognise situations to which the four operations apply.

Materials

paper to fold

Focus

These pages explore word problems that require addition, subtraction, multiplication and an understanding of place value. The wording is more complex than in the previous problems that involved a combination of the three operations. Pupils need to determine what the problem is asking and, in many cases, carry out more than one equation in order to find solutions. Materials can be used to assist with the calculation if necessary, as these problems are about reading for information and determining what the problem is asking rather than computation or basic facts.

Discussion

Page 43

The problems mostly require multiplication, with some addition and subtraction. Each problem is fairly straightforward, with all the information needed to find a solution readily available. The numbers have been kept simple to assist with the problem-solving process and there is no additional information that is not needed.

Pupils may find it helpful to draw a diagram in order to work out what is happening in the problem and to determine what needs to be multiplied to provide a solution. Addition can be used at times rather than multiplication.

Page 44

This investigation provides information about a library, with a number of interrelated questions arising from it. The questions begin with a set number of books, magazines and CD-ROMs. Using this information as a basis, the numbers of each item are changed to meet new criteria, with some books, magazines and CD-ROMs being borrowed, returned, shelved and dusted. Pupils are required to keep track of the new information and use it to answer the subsequent questions.

Computation is not always needed to find a solution; for example, Problem 1 states that each shelf holds 100 books and, as there are 9472 books in the library, 95 shelves are needed. No division is necessary as place value tells us that 9472 has 94 hundreds, so 95 shelves must be needed. Similarly with Problem 2, 48 shelves are being dusted, which means 48 hundreds. Therefore, 4800 books have been dusted.

Page 45

A careful reading of each problem is needed to determine what the problem is asking. These problems focus around trains, carriages, people and seats. In some problems people are getting on and getting off and in others it is necessary to determine how many people are sitting or standing in a carriage. Each problem requires more than one step and two or more operations are needed to find a solution. There are a number of ways to find solutions and pupils should be encouraged to explore and try different possibilities of arriving at solutions.

Possible difficulties

- Inability to identify the need to add, subtract or multiply
- Not using place value concepts to solve the problems
- Confusion over the need to carry out more than one step to arrive at a solution
- Not understanding the concept of 'capacity'

Extension

- Pupils could write their own problems and give them to other pupils to solve.

BEADING

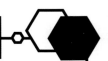

1. Judy has 6 bags of coloured beads, with 42 beads in each bag. If she uses 29 beads to make a necklace, how many beads does she have left?

_____

2. Manu has 7 bags of beads. He buys 2 more bags and uses 25 beads to make some bracelets. If each bag contains 32 beads, how many beads does he have now?

_____

3. Clarence bought 3 bags of beads on Monday, 5 bags on Tuesday and 4 bags on Wednesday. Each bag contains 48 beads. How many beads did he buy?

_____

4. Mandy has 25 bags of beads. She gives 6 bags to her friend, Elly, and 8 bags to her other friend, Sarah. If each bag holds 36 beads, how many beads did she give away?

_____

5. Ned has 4 large bags of beads and 7 small bags of beads. The large bags hold 25 beads and the small bags hold 15 beads. He uses 24 beads to make a necklace and 18 beads per bracelet to make two bracelets. How many beads does he have now?

_____

6. Zena has 7 bags of beads, with 30 beads in each bag. She used 36 beads to make 2 necklaces and 54 beads to make 6 bracelets. She wants to make the same set of jewellery tomorrow. Does she have enough beads?

_____

LIBRARY

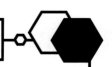

The library has books, magazines and CD-ROMs. It has a total stock of 9472 books, 315 magazines and 143 CD-ROMs.

1. In the library, each set of shelves holds 100 books. How many sets of shelves are needed to hold all of the books?

   _____

2. The cleaner has dusted 48 sets of shelves. How many books have been dusted?

   _____

3. (a) At the start of the day, the library's computer showed there were 6841 books currently in the library. During the morning, 275 books were taken out and 97 books returned and during the afternoon, 166 books were taken out and 134 returned. How many books are now in the library?

   _____

   (b) Later in the day, six boxes of books, two boxes of magazines and four boxes of CD-ROMs were delivered to the library. If each box of books holds 65 books, how many books are now in the library?

   _____

4. Every pupil in Year Four borrowed a book from the library. If there are 4 classes with 26 pupils in each class, how many books were borrowed?

   _____

5. During stocktaking, 284 old and damaged books were removed from the shelves to be packed into boxes. If each box can hold 10 books, how many boxes are needed to pack all of the books?

   _____

AT THE STATION

1. There were 604 people on the train. At the first station, 58 people got on and 129 people got off. At the next station, 143 people got on and 72 people got off. How many people are now on the train?

_____

2. The train has 12 carriages. Each carriage has 47 seats and can hold 65 people.

   (a) How many people can sit on the train? _____

   (b) How many people can travel on the train? _____

3. There are 36 people in the first carriage, 27 people in the second carriage and 46 people in the third carriage. Each carriage is able to hold 60 people. How many more people are needed to fill the train to capacity?

   _____

4. There are 9 carriages and each carriage is able to hold 65 people. After stopping at the fifth station there are 329 people on the train. How many more people can board the train before it is full?

   _____

5. The train has 8 carriages and each carriage has 47 seats. There are 411 people on the train. If every seat has one person on it, how many people are not sitting down?

   _____

6. At the first station, 63 people got on and 138 people got off. At the next station, 94 people got on and 86 people got off. There are now 261 people on the train. How many people were on the train to begin with?

   _____

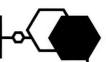

Problem-solving

To read, interpret and analyse information.

Curriculum links

England (Year 4)

- Using and applying: Solve one-step and two-step problems involving numbers and choose and carry out appropriate calculations.
- Using and applying: Report solutions to puzzles and problems.
- Calculating: Add or subtract mentally two-digit whole numbers.
- Calculating: Use efficient written methods to add and subtract two- and three-digit whole numbers.
- Calculating: Use written methods for multiplication and division.

Northern Ireland (Key Stage 2)

- Processes in maths: Develop a range of strategies for problem solving, looking for ways to overcome difficulties.
- Number: Develop an understanding of place value.
- Number: Develop strategies to add and subtract mentally.
- Number: Engage in a range of activities to develop understanding of the four operations of number, and use these operations to solve problems.

Scotland (First and Second)

- Number processes: Explain the link between a digit, its place and its value (1st).
- +/-/x/÷: Use addition, subtraction, multiplication and division when solving problems, making best use of the mental strategies and written skills developed (1st).
- +/-/x/÷: Determine which calculations are needed to solve problems involving whole numbers (2nd).

Wales (Key Stage 2)

- Skills: Select and use the appropriate mathematics to solve problems in a variety of contexts.
- Skills: Use effective methods of computation.
- Skills: Develop a variety of mental and written strategies of computation.
- Number: Understand place value in relation to the position of digits.
- Number: Use a variety of mental methods of computation and extend written methods.
- Number: Recognise situations to which the four operations apply.

Materials

calculator, number expander

Focus

Pupils explore concepts of place value and number sense. The relationships among numbers and place value are analysed. and pupils are encouraged to find suitable numbers and disregard numbers that are not possible. Place value and number sense are needed rather than division.

Discussion

Page 47

Pupils need to read and interpret information and use it in the context of place value. As the book has 10 equal-length chapters, an understanding of place value can be used to solve each problem. Given that the book has 690 pages we know that this number has a place value of 69 tens, so each chapter must be 69 pages long. This information can be used to calculate the various problems.

Before starting, pupils may find it helpful to draw up a table outlining the starting page of each chapter. We know that each chapter has 69 pages and that Chapter 1 starts on page 1, so Chapter 2 must start on page 70 and so on.

The page number that Walter has read to is given at the beginning and this information is needed to answer some of the problems. For example, in order to determine how many pages Walter has read past the middle of the book and needs read to finish the book, it is necessary to keep in mind that there are 690 pages in the book and he has read up to page 437.

Possible difficulties

- Not considering place value to solve the questions
- Not taking into consideration the starting page of each chapter

Extension

- Change the criteria involving the number of pages in the book and the page number read to and explore the problems again based on the new criteria.

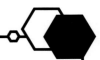

BOOKWORMS

Walter's book starts on page 1 and has 690 pages. There are 10 equal-length chapters in the book and he has read up to page 437.

1. How many pages are in each chapter?

2. Walter's favourite page is 409. Is it in Chapter 7?

3. Walter reads 10 pages each morning and 10 pages each night. How long has he been reading this book?

4. How many pages past the middle of the book has he read?

5. Walter's favourite chapter is Chapter 3. From starting page to finish, what pages are in Chapter 3?

6. The most exciting part was from pages 351 to 379. What chapter are they in?

7. How many more pages does he have to read to finish the book?

8. Walter's sister is also reading this book. She has read eight pages of Chapter 6. What page is she up to?

9. How many more pages does she need to read to finish the book?

10. If she reads 10 pages a day, how long will it take her to finish the book?

Prim-Ed Publishing®   www.prim-ed.com

Problem-solving in mathematics

Problem-solving

To use spatial visualisation, logical reasoning and measurement to solve problems.

Curriculum links

England (Year 4)
- Using and applying: Solve one-step and two-step problems involving numbers, money and measures and choose and carry out appropriate calculations.
- Using and applying: Report solutions to puzzles and problems.
- Counting and understanding number: Use decimal notation for money and measurement.
- Calculating: Use efficient written methods to add and subtract two- and three-digit whole numbers.
- Calculating: Use written methods for multiplication.
- Calculating: Use a calculator to carry out one-step and two-step calculations involving all four operations.
- Measuring: Calculate perimeters and find the area of rectilinear shapes.

Northern Ireland (Key Stage 2)
- Processes in maths: Develop a range of strategies for problem solving, looking for ways to overcome difficulties.
- Number: Engage in a range of activities to develop understanding of the four operations of number, and use these operations to solve problems.
- Number: Use the four operations to solve problems involving money.
- Measures: Use the four operations to solve measures problems.
- Measures: Calculate perimeter and area.

Scotland (First and Second)
- +/-/x: Use addition, subtraction and multiplication when solving problems, making best use of the mental strategies and written skills developed (1ˢᵗ).
- +/-/x: Determine which calculations are needed to solve problems involving whole numbers (2ⁿᵈ).
- +/-/x: Solve problems involving decimals using a variety of methods (2ⁿᵈ).
- Measurement: Carry out calculations when solving measurement problems (2ⁿᵈ).
- Measurement: Find the perimeter and area of 2-D shapes (2ⁿᵈ).

Wales (Key Stage 2)
- Skills: Select and use the appropriate mathematics to solve problems in a variety of contexts.
- Skills: Use effective methods of computation.
- Skills: Develop a variety of mental and written strategies of computation.
- Number: Use a variety of mental methods of computation and extend written methods.
- Number: Recognise situations to which the four operations apply.
- Measures and money: Find perimeters and areas of simple shapes.
- Measures and money: Use the four operations to solve problems involving money.

Materials

paper to fold

Focus

These pages explore different ways of visualising problems and analysing the possibilities that make up the whole solution.

Logical reasoning is required, as well as an understanding of measurement (kilometres, metres and centimetres). In each situation, diagrams can be used to organise, sort and explore the data.

Discussion

Page 49

In these problems, pupils need to visualise the paths that the farmer and dog take as they travel around the outside of each shape. Some of the lengths around the paddock and garden need to be determined from the diagrams and an ability to rename from kilometres to metres or centimetres to metres is required.

In the first problem, the farmer rides around the paddock more than two times, passing by corners B, C and D three times. The distance around the paddock is 5300 m which can be used, along with the distance from A to D, to calculate the distance travelled to return to D. For Problem 2, interpreting the diagram to determine the lengths is more complex, although some pupils may realise that finding the distance all around three times and then subtracting the distance from G to A is simpler.

Page 50

The problems on this page are essentially solved the same way; however, the provision of the image of a balance for the first problem makes it is easier to see how the mango from the top picture can be substituted using the scales in the second picture. Problem 2 requires more complex thinking.

One approach is to create a table of possible values using a process of 'try and adjust':

6 rolls and 1 loaf costs £4.20					
roll	6 rolls	loaf	4 rolls	2 loaves	Total
0.50	3.00	1.20	2.00	2.40	5.40 – too little
0.40	2.40	1.80	1.60	3.60	5.20 – too little
0.35	2.10	2.10	1.40	4.20	5.60 – too much
0.30	1.80	2.40	1.20	4.80	6.00
A loaf of bread costs £2.40. A bread roll costs 30p.					

Page 51

This page extends the thinking about perimeters explored on page 39. With Problem 1, when the paper is folded four squares will result. Since the length of each side of the small square is 3 cm, each will have an area of 9 cm², so the area of the original square must be 36 cm². Alternatively, the large square has sides of 6 cm in length, giving an area of 36 cm². The second problem requires pupils to visualise the relationships among the squares and determine the area after the length of its sides is known.

Possible difficulties

- Unable to rename centimetres to metres or metres to kilometres
- Not using the given data to determine the sides whose length is not stated
- Unable to see how the information in the problems can balance
- Unsure of the area of a square and confusing it with perimeter

Extension

- Pupils could write their own problems involving distance around an irregular shape where some of the lengths have to be worked out from the information in the diagrams. Other problems could involve items on a balance or areas cut from inside an arrangement of shapes. The problems are then given to other pupils to solve.

FARM TRAILS

1. A farmer started at corner A of the paddock and rode his trail bike around the perimeter to see if there were any gaps in the fence. He found one hole at D and continued all the way around to A, where he picked up his tools to fix the fence. He then rode to D and fixed the hole.

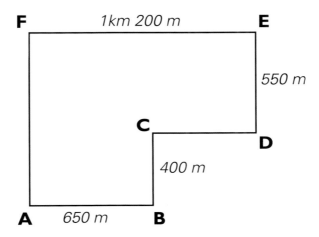

To be sure the fence was completely free of holes, he rode all the way around once more until he arrived at D again.

How far did he ride to check and fix the fence? _____

2. When he got back to the farmhouse, he picked some vegetables from the garden. His dog, Blue, wasn't allowed in the garden, so he walked around the outside fence, starting at A. He ran around and around anticlockwise, only stopping when he reached G for the third time.

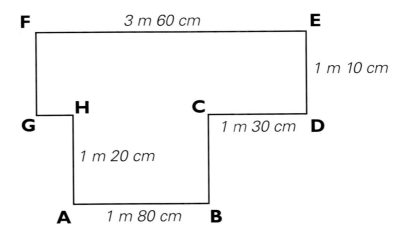

How far did Blue walk? _____

13 lychees weigh as much as two bananas and one mango.

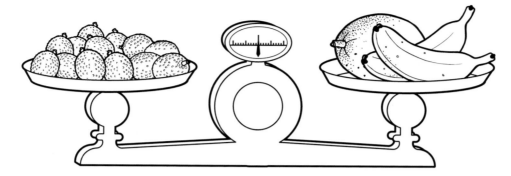

Four lychees and one banana have the same weight as one mango.

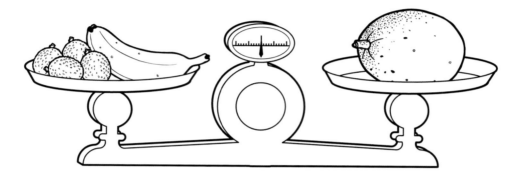

1. How many lychees are needed to balance one mango? _____

Six bread rolls and one loaf of bread cost £4.20.

Four bread rolls and two loaves of bread cost £6.00.

2. What is the price of a loaf of bread?

_____

3. What is the price of a bread roll?

_____

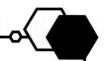

SQUARES AND AREA

Area is the amount of surface covered.

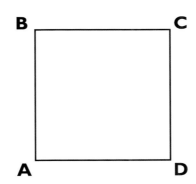

ABCD is a square sheet of paper.

Imagine that you fold the paper so that corner A folds onto corner D and corner B folds onto corner C.

Now imagine that you fold it again so that A folds onto C.

The length of one side of the folded shape is 3 cm.

1. What is the area of the square ABCD? _____

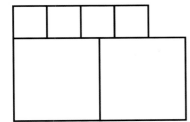

This shape is made up of four small squares (each with sides of 5 cm) and two large squares (with sides of 12 cm).

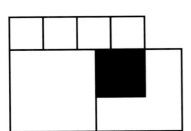

A square hole is cut out of the shape as shown.

2. What is the area of the hole?

_____

3. What is the area of the L shape around the hole? _____

Problem-solving

To solve problems involving time or coordinates and to make decisions based on particular criteria

Curriculum links

England (Year 4)

- Using and applying: Solve one-step and two-step problems involving numbers or measures and choose and carry out appropriate calculations.
- Using and applying: Report solutions to puzzles and problems.
- Understanding shape: Describe and identify the position of a square on a grid of squares.
- Measuring: Calculate time intervals from timetables.

Northern Ireland (Key Stage 2)

- Processes in maths: Develop a range of strategies for problem solving, looking for ways to overcome difficulties.
- Measures: Recognise times on digital clocks, understand the relationship between the 12- and 24-hour clocks and use timetables.
- Shape and space: Use co-ordinates.

Scotland (First and Second)

- Time: Use timetables and schedules to plan events and activities, and make time calculations as part of planning (2nd).
- Angle, symmetry and transformation: Use co-ordinate system to plot and describe the location of a point on a grid (2nd).

Wales (Key Stage 2)

- Skills: Select and use the appropriate mathematics to solve problems in a variety of contexts.
- Measures and money: Read times on digital clocks, use timetables, convert between 12- and 24-hour clocks and calculate time differences.
- Shape, position and movement: Use positive co-ordinates to specify location.

Materials

digital clock, 0–99 number board

Focus

These pages focus on reading for information, obtaining information from a number of sources and using it to find solutions. The problems involve thinking and working with time and coordinates. Decisions based on times being 'earliest' or 'latest' are needed as well as exact time.

Discussion

Page 53

This worksheet requires pupils to read for information and decide what information answers different criteria. The concepts of 'earliest' and 'latest' are used in a number of the problems rather than exact time. The ideas of the 'longest opening day' as well as the 'longest opening times' are explored.

Page 54

These problems involve following directions and using coordinates. With Question 1, pupils plot the path of a car using the given coordinates. They need to keep in mind that the first digit in each pair is across (x axis) while the second digit is up (y axis). Question 2 requires the pupils to provide the coordinates that describe a given path. The final question requires them to coordinate drawing a path and recording the coordinates.

Page 55

This page explores pupils' understanding of 24-hour digital time as they investigate the ways in which the digits can be placed to show possible times and determine the time closest to midday and midnight. The way in which zero is used on a digital clock also needs to be considered. There are 24 possibilities as there cannot be 90, 91 or 92 minutes, but '0' is used to show the hour after midnight. For Problem 2 an understanding of two-digit numbers needs to be coordinated with an understanding of how and when the digits change on a digital clock. Thinking about the two-digit numbers suggest where '2' will occur in the ones or tens place and how long, the '2' will remain displayed until it changes to a '3'. For example, when '2' occurs in the hour display (e.g. 2:00, 12:00, 20:00) it remains unchanging for the whole of the hour so it should be counted just once.

Extension

- Use the information and timetable to write other questions.
- Construct a similar timetable for two pizza shops where one opens for lunch and dinner and the other just for dinner.
- Have pupils call out the coordinates they have drawn to other pupils to construct the path and compare results.

DVD RENTALS

DVD Easy		Hours open
Monday	CLOSED	
Tuesday	11:00 am to 8:00 pm	
Wednesday	11:00 am to 9:00 pm	
Thursday	10:00 am to 9:00 pm	
Friday	11:00 am to 10:00 pm	
Saturday	10:00 am to 10:00 pm	
Sunday	11:00 am to 9:00 pm	
	Total hours	

DVD Rentals		Hours open
Monday	11:00 am to 9:00 pm	
Tuesday	11:00 am to 9:00 pm	
Wednesday	CLOSED	
Thursday	11:00 am to 9:00 pm	
Friday	11:00 am to 11:00 pm	
Saturday	10:00 am to 11:00 pm	
Sunday	11:00 am to 9:00 pm	
	Total hours	

1. What is the difference between the amount of time both shops are open in one week?

   _____

2. What is the latest time that a DVD can be hired on the weekend?

   _____

3. What is the earliest time that a DVD can be hired during the week?

   _____

4. Which shop has the day with the longest opening hours?

   _____

5. Which day has the longest opening hours?

   _____

6. Which shop would I use if I wanted to hire a DVD on Tuesday at 2:00 pm?

   _____

7. Which shop would I use if I wanted to hire a DVD on Monday at 11:00 am?

   _____

8. Circle the correct answer.

   Can I hire a DVD on:

   (a) Wednesday at 3:00 pm from DVD Rentals?   YES   NO
   (b) Saturday at 10:00 am?   YES   NO
   (c) Friday at 10:30 pm?   YES   NO
   (d) Wednesday at DVD Easy?   YES   NO
   (e) Thursday at 10:30 pm?   YES   NO

Prim-Ed Publishing®   www.prim-ed.com

DRIVE TIME

1. Follow the coordinates to draw the paths of the cars.

(a)

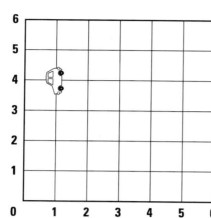

Car One
(1,4)(1,1)(3,1)(3,3)
(2,3)(2,5)(5,5)(5,1)

Car Two
(1,5)(2,5)(2,3)(4,3)
(4,4)(3,4)(3,5)(5,5)
(5,1)(3,1)(1,1)(1,2)

(b)

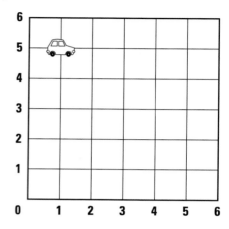

2. Write the coordinates of each car's path.

(a)

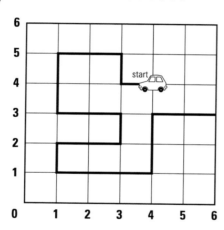

Car Three
_____
_____
_____

Car Four
_____
_____
_____

(b)

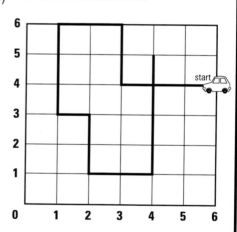

3. Draw your own path and write the coordinates to match.

(a)

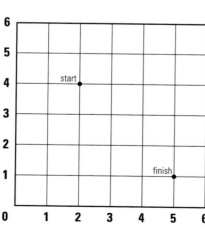

Car Five
_____
_____
_____

Car Six
_____
_____
_____

(b)

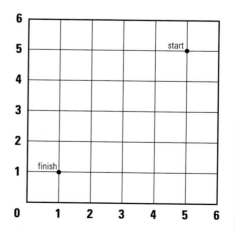

www.prim-ed.com   Prim-Ed Publishing®

CLOCK WATCHING

A digital clock has been set to show 24-hour time.

1. (a) What times can be shown using only the digits 0, 1, 2 and 9?

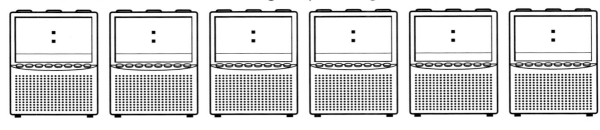

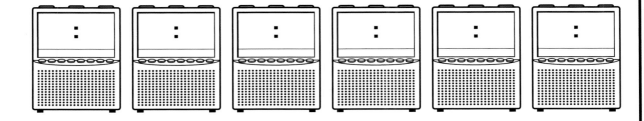

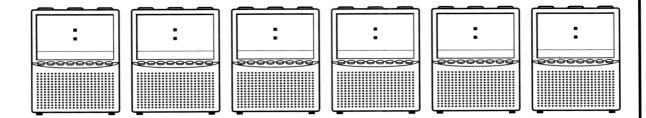

   (b) What time is closest to midday? _____

   (c) What time is closest to midnight? _____

2. If you watched this clock all day, how many times would the digit '2' be displayed:

   (a) to show minutes each hour? _____

   (b) to show minutes in 24 hours? _____

   (c) to show hours in 24 hours? _____

3. Total number of times '2' is displayed in 24 hours. _____

Problem-solving

To use strategic thinking to solve problems.

Curriculum links

England (Year 4)
- Using and applying: Solve one-step and two-step problems involving numbers and money and choose and carry out appropriate calculations.
- Using and applying: Report solutions to puzzles and problems.
- Calculating: Use efficient written methods to add and subtract two- and three-digit whole numbers.
- Calculating: Use written methods for multiplication and division.
- Calculating: Use a calculator to carry out one-step and two-step calculations involving all four operations.

Northern Ireland (Key Stage 2)
- Processes in maths: Develop a range of strategies for problem solving, looking for ways to overcome difficulties.
- Number: Engage in a range of activities to develop understanding of the four operations of number, and use these operations to solve problems.
- Number: Use the four operations to solve problems involving money.

Scotland (First and Second)
- +/-/x/÷: Use addition, subtraction, multiplication and division when solving problems, making best use of the mental strategies and written skills developed (1st).
- +/-/x/÷: Determine which calculations are needed to solve problems involving whole numbers (2nd).

Wales (Key Stage 2)
- Skills: Select and use the appropriate mathematics to solve problems in a variety of contexts.
- Skills: Use effective methods of computation.
- Skills: Develop a variety of mental and written strategies of computation.
- Number: Use a variety of mental methods of computation and extend written methods.
- Number: Recognise situations to which the four operations apply.
- Measures and money: Use the four operations to solve problems involving money.

Materials

counters

Focus

These pages explore problems that may have several answers and further analysis of the connections among the data is needed to see whether this is the case or whether there is only one solution. A process of 'try and adjust' could be used; however, using logical reasoning to think about possibilities and using a table, diagram or materials to organise them will be more productive.

These ways of thinking can then be used to solve other complex problems.

Discussion

Page 57

There are several ways these problems can be solved. Emus have two legs and alpaca have four legs. Since there are 38 heads, there must be 38 animals altogether. If all of the animals were emus, there would only be 76 legs. The remaining 24 legs must belong to the alpacas. Since an alpaca has two more legs than an emu, there would be 12 alpacas and 26 emus (a total of 100 legs).

Another way would be to put multiples of two or four into a table or diagram and systematically check the remaining numbers until a solution is reached. Counters could also be used to model the problem, again focusing on groups of two and four.

The second problem can be solved in the same way, while a table or counters will also assist with Problem 3. Since she sells twice as many emus as alpacas, she must receive £72 for each alpaca and two emus. Since 15 x 72 is £1080, she sold 15 alpacas.

Page 58

The first two problems can be solved in the same way as on page 57. However, Question 3 does not give a second condition and there are several possibilities. As the animals have either two or four legs, an odd number of chickens will not be possible.

Page 59

These problems require careful reading to see how the information needs to be used. Some children may simply try to subtract the smaller number from the larger for the first two problems. However, it is the expression 'more than' that is critical in each case. Subtraction gives the difference between the two prices and the actual amounts need to be found to match both the total and the difference. In Problem 3, many pupils may at first just share the money among the four, whereas these amounts need to match both the condition of equalling £1200 and keeping a difference of £100 between each amount.

Possible difficulties
- Not using a table or diagram to manage the data
- Not considering all the possible answers—there may be more than one possibility
- Only keeping one condition in mind when there are two aspects to consider and reconcile

Extension
- Discuss the various methods used by pupils to solve the problem. Include the ones discussed above. Ask them to solve each problem using a different method to that they used or first tried. Encourage them to use a diagram rather than simply calculate.

ON THE FARM

1. A farmer had a number of emus and alpacas in one paddock. When she counted, there were 38 heads and 100 legs. How many emus and how many alpacas were in the paddock?

2. The farmer decided to buy some young calves and piglets at the market. She paid £60 for each piglet and £95 for each calf. She paid for the 10 animals she bought with a cheque for £740. How many calves and how many piglets did she buy?

3. Her neighbour needed to buy more stock, so the farmer sold him some alpacas for £48 and twice as many emus for £12 each. She received a total of £1080. How many alpacas and how many emus did she sell?

IN THE BARN

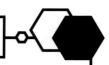

1. The farm workers keep their farm bikes in the barn. Some of the workers have bikes with 2 wheels and some have bikes with 3 wheels, but all of the bikes have 2 handles. Peter, one of the farmhands, counts the handles on the bikes and gets a total of 50. He also counts a total number of 64 wheels on the bikes. How many of the bikes have 3 wheels and how many have 2 wheels?

2. There are many spiders and beetles in the barn. One of the workers collects some of each. She notices that there are 200 legs and 29 bodies. How many spiders and how many beetles are in her collection?

3. When the weather turns cold, the farmer puts her young calves and chickens in the barn to keep warm. As she puts them in the warmth, she notices that there are a total of 28 legs. How many calves and how many chickens are there?

MARKET DAY

1. At the market, the farmer bought a pig and a piglet for £300. If the pig cost £250 more than the piglet, what did she pay for the pig?

2. When the farmer sold a cow and her calf, she received £480. She noticed that the cow sold for £278 more than the calf. How much did the cow sell for?

3. The farmer had four sons, aged 12, 14, 15 and 16. In their spare time, they took the vegetables they grew to the market and sold them for £1200. Since they did not all work as hard as each other in the vegetable garden, they decided to divide the money so that each brother got £100 more than his next younger brother. How much did the youngest brother get?

Problem-solving

To use logical reasoning and spatial visualisation to solve problems.

Curriculum links

England (Year 4)
- Using and applying: Solve one-step and two-step problems involving numbers and money and choose and carry out appropriate calculations.
- Using and applying: Report solutions to puzzles and problems.
- Calculating: Use efficient written methods to add and subtract two- and three-digit whole numbers.
- Calculating: Use written methods for multiplication and division.
- Calculating: Find fractions of numbers.
- Calculating: Use a calculator to carry out one-step and two-step calculations involving all four operations.

Northern Ireland (Key Stage 2)
- Processes in maths: Develop a range of strategies for problem solving, looking for ways to overcome difficulties.
- Number: Understand and use fractions.
- Number: Engage in a range of activities to develop understanding of the four operations of number, and use these operations to solve problems.
- Number: Use the four operations to solve problems involving money.

Scotland (First and Second)
- +/-/x/÷: Use addition, subtraction, multiplication and division when solving problems, making best use of the mental strategies and written skills developed (1st).
- +/-/x/÷: Determine which calculations are needed to solve problems involving whole numbers (2nd).
- Fractions: Find a fraction of an amount by applying my knowledge of division (1st).
- Fractions: Investigate everyday contexts in which fractions are used and carry out calculations to solve related problems (2nd).

Wales (Key Stage 2)
- Skills: Select and use the appropriate mathematics to solve problems in a variety of contexts.
- Skills: Use effective methods of computation.
- Skills: Develop a variety of mental and written strategies of computation.
- Number: Use a variety of mental methods of computation and extend written methods.
- Number: Recognise situations to which the four operations apply.
- Number: Calculate fractions of quantities.
- Measures and money: Use the four operations to solve problems involving money.

Materials

counters, base 10 materials

Focus

These pages explore problems based on a conceptual understanding of fractions. Writing the fractions using numbers and words is designed to help pupils focus on the number of parts as well as their comparative sizes and to lead them to consider other ways of solving the problems other than by fraction calculations. One way of solving them is by backtracking from the answers. Counters can

be useful as they allow the parts to be considered while the whole problem is also kept in mind. Using a diagram is another method and is probably a different way of thinking about fractions than is used by many pupils and teachers.

Discussion

Page 61
These problems can be used as a consolidation of the 'analyse-explore-try' model of problem-solving that has evolved over the varied number, spatial and measurement situations posed in this book. This is discussed in detail in the introduction (pages xiv-xvi). In these problems the information needs to be carefully analysed to determine how much money was available at the beginning rather than at the end of a situation. In this way, some pupils may think of what they did for the questions on page 19 as a guide to these. Pupils could use counters or base 10 materials to represent the questions as they are worked through either forwards or backwards. Using 'try and adjust' is another possible way towards a solution.

Another way of thinking that can be used is to use a diagram as on page xiii.

Placing the amounts involved in Question 2 in a diagram (as shown below) can help. Peter originally spent two-thirds of his total amount on the present.

This is represented by the two shaded blocks.

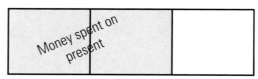

With the third left, he spent 1 third of the amount on wrapping and a card. This is represented by the shading in the final block.

The £18 he could spend on himself is shown by the two unshaded parts of the diagram. This means that each of the two parts must be £9 and he took 9 x £9, or £81 in total, to shop with.

Possible difficulties
- Not confident working with fractions
- Thinking that 1 third and 1 half gives 1 fifth
- Thinking that 2 thirds of Peter's initial money, together with 1 third of what is left, must account for all of his money
- Not being able to consider using materials or a diagram and attempting a solution on the basis of calculations

Extension
- Change the fraction amounts but leave the problem statements the same.
- Change the problem contexts but leave the fraction amounts the same.
- Have pupils make up problems of their own and challenge others to solve them using diagrams.

1. On Saturday, Peta went to the shopping centre to buy a new outfit to wear to her friend's birthday party. She spent half of her money on a dress and then 1 third of what she had left on a pair of sandals. She was left with £60.00 in her purse. How much money did she have to start with?

2. On Sunday, her brother, Peter, went to the shopping centre to buy a birthday present for the party. He spent 2 thirds of his money on the present and then spent 1 third of what he had left for a card and wrapping paper. That left him with £18 to buy something for himself. How much money did he originally have when he went shopping?

SOLUTIONS

Note: Many solutions are written statements rather than just numbers. This is to encourage teachers and pupils to solve problems in this way.

STACKING SHAPES ....Page 3

1. 30 cubes
2. 20 oranges
3. 50 cans
4. 36 cubes

PAINTED CUBES ....Page 4

1. 4 cubes
2. 3 cubes
3. 1 cube
4. 4 cubes
5. 8 cubes
6. 4 cubes
7. No cube has only 1, 5 or 6 faces on the outside of the block.

CUBE PAINTING.................................Page 5

1. 8 cubes
2. Yes
3. 1 cube
4.

No. of faces painted	No. of cubes
0	1
1	6
2	12
3	8
Total = 27	

5. Answers will vary

HOW MANY DIGITS? ....Page 7

1. (a) 140
   (b) 140
2. (a) less (you would exclude 'fifty' and 'fifteen')
   (b) 118
   (c) 140
3. 2 and 3 – say: 118 times, write: 140 times; 6 to 9 – say: 140 times; write: 140 times

STAR GAZE.......................................Page 9

1. (a) 23   (b) 55   (c) 95
2. (a)  (b) (c)

   (d)  (e) (f)

   (g) (h) (i)

MAGIC SQUARES..............................Page 10

1. 12
2. (a)

15	1	11
5	9	13
7	17	3

27   (b) All odd numbers

3.

11	4	9
6	8	10
7	12	5

24

4.

16	3	2	13
5	10	11	8
9	6	7	12
4	15	14	1

34

5. 34
6. 34
7. 34
8. 1–16
9. 1514 in the middle two squares in the bottom row.

SUDOKU ....Page 11

1.

1	2	4	3
3	4	1	2
2	1	3	4
4	3	2	1

2.

3	1	4	2
2	4	1	3
1	3	2	4
4	2	3	1

3.

3	1	2	4
4	2	3	1
1	3	4	2
2	4	1	3

4.

4	1	2	3
3	2	1	4
1	4	3	2
2	3	4	1

THE WATER PARK..............................Page 13

1. 301 more adults
2. 433 people swimming in the pools
3. 108 people lying on their towels
4. 100 people floating on swimming mats
5. 150 people
6. 37 surfers did not catch a wave.

SOLUTIONS

Note: Many solutions are written statements rather than just numbers. This is to encourage teachers and pupils to solve problems in this way.

LILY PADS AND FROGS ....Page 14
1. 261 flowers
2. 192 lily pads
3. 111 frogs
4. 125 lily pads are in flower
5. Yes, there are 375 flowers
6. 333 lily pads
7. 410 frogs stayed behind during summer.

GONE FISHING ....Page 15
1. 278 yabbies were caught.
2. 141 more bass were caught.
3. 187 perch have not been caught.
4. Second weekend
5. First weekend
6. First weekend: 282 fish were caught—yabbies are not fish.

CHICKEN TAKEAWAY ....Page 17
1. Spent: £9.00
2. Spent: £24.50
3. Spent: £19.00, change: £31.00
4. Spent: £35.50, change: £14.50
5. Spent: £30.00, change: £20.00
6. Spent: £31.00, change: £19.00
7. Salam

THE BIG RACE ....Page 19
1. 14th place
2. 14 cars
3. ninth place
4. 11th

SERIAL NUMBERS ....Page 20
1. 3946
2. 5723
3. 2835 or 5382

PUZZLE SCROLLS ....Page 21
1. 95 and 96
2. 100 cards
3. eight triangles
4. Sunday is the first day of the month. Tuesday is the last day of the month.
5. If he used a 30cm ruler—62 m
   If he used a 1m ruler—60 m 60 cm or 60.6 m
6. These digits could also be rearranged: 953, 539, 593, 359, 395. There are also other possibilities: 179, 197,

719, 791, 917, 971, 278, 287, 728, 782, 827, 872, 359, 395, 539, 593, 935, 953, 467, 476, 647, 674, 746, 764, 458, 485, 548, 584, 845, 854, 962, 926, 296, 269, 692, 629.

SAMANTHA'S FLOWER SHOP ....Page 23
1. 54 pots are available for sale
2. (a) Yes   (b)   68 roses to sell
3. Yes, with 22 roses left over.
4. (a)   35 lilies are left over.
   (b)   75 lilies

HERB MARKET ....Page 24
1. 155 more fresh herbs.
2. Simon has 144 pots.
3. Simon needs 360 seeds.
4. He can sell 195 bunches.
5. He has 106 bunches left.
6. none
7. He has unpacked 60 plants.

AT THE BAKERY ....Page 25
1. She needs to bake 226 cakes.
2. 316 wholemeal loaves were sold.
3. (a)   There are 180 pies available to sell.
   (b)   97 pies were not sold.
4. There are 44 fairy cakes available to sell.

NUMBERS IN COLUMNS ....Page 27
1. E
2. (a) D   (b) A   (c) D   (d) B   (e) C
3. (a) 7   (b) 13   (c) 18   (d) 19   (e) 22
4. Answers will vary—Each ones place value amount is repeated in the same column. With the rows, numbers with the same tens place value appear in rows of threes, overlapping with the previous tens place value.
5. Answer will vary—Each ones place value amount is repeated in the same column.
6. Yes, numbers with 4 in the ones place are still in Column D; numbers with 1 in the ones place will be in Column A.

CALCULATOR PROBLEMS ....Page 29
1. 5675
2. 6976
3. 13 396
4. 9658
5. 7739
6. 6095

SOLUTIONS

Note: Many solutions are written statements rather than just numbers. This is to encourage teachers and pupils to solve problems in this way.

ICE-CREAM CONES .... Page 30

1. Anna has 2490 cones.
2. They need 60 cartons.
3. 4970 cones were delivered.
4. 10 930 cones are left.
5. The shop has 2820 cones.
6. The shop has 24 extra boxes.

CHOCOLATE FROGS .... Page 31

1. Trudy has wrapped 36 chocolate frogs.
2. (a) 8 and 1   (b) 2 and 7   (c) 3 and 6   (d) 4 and 5
3. (a) 1, 8, 2, 7   (b) 3, 6, 4, 5

                   or

   (a) 1, 8, 3, 6   (b) 2, 7, 5, 4

                   or

   (a) 1, 8, 5, 4   (b) 2, 7, 3, 6
4. (a) 1, 3, 8   (b) 2, 4, 6

                   or

   (a) 2, 3, 7   (b) 1, 5, 6

HOW MANY? .... Page 33

1. 590 390 visitors in 2006
2. 131 000 visitors in January
3. 33 370 visitors in June

HOW FAR? .... Page 34

1. Erin travelled 680 km.
2. Susie swims about 6 km (6000 m).
3. It will arrive 6 hours and 24 minutes after leaving.
4. Brian runs about 700 km.
5. Kim-Ly travelled 650 km

HOW MUCH? .... Page 35

1. Derek spent £80 on towels.
2. Payment per paper is £35.86. Hourly payment is £25.25.
3. Alison sold 60 apples.
4. Brackets without screws are 20p cheaper.
5. Payment per tree is £355.20, payment per day is £317.50.

SPANISH HOLIDAY .... Page 37

1. ST47, ST51, ST68, LA321, LA471, LA511
2. ST23, ST32, LA231
3. ST74, LA681, LA741

SQUARES AND PERIMETERS .... Page 39

1. (a) 30 cm   (b) 36 cm   (c) 30 cm   (d) 42 cm
   (e) 48 cm   (f) 36 cm   (g) 30 cm

2. Teacher check
3. Answers will vary

MORE PERIMETERS .... Page 40

1. (a) A smaller square   (b) 8 cm
2. A small triangle
3. 18 cm
4. 48 cm

PERIMETERS IN SQUARES .... Page 41

1. 24 cm
2. 72 cm
3. 80 m

BEADING .... Page 43

1. Judy has 223 beads left.
2. Manu has 263 beads.
3. Clarence bought 576 beads.
4. Mandy gave away 504 beads.
5. Ned has 145 beads.
6. Yes, she has 210 beads and uses 180 beads.

LIBRARY .... Page 44

1. 95 shelves are needed.
2. The cleaner dusted 4800 books.
3. (a) There are 6631 books.
   (b) The library has 7021 books.
4. 104 books were borrowed.
5. 29 boxes are needed.

AT THE STATION .... Page 45

1. 604 people are on the train.
2. (a) 564 people are seated.
   (b) 780 people can travel on the train.
3. 71 more people are needed to fill the train.
4. 256 more people can board the train.
5. 35 people are standing.
6. There were 328 people on the train to begin with.

BOOKWORMS .... Page 47

1. 69 pages in each chapter.
2. No, it is in Chapter 6.
3. Walter has been reading his books for 22 days.
4. Walter has read 92 pages past the middle of the book.
5. Pages 139–207
6. Chapter 6
7. He needs to read 253 pages to finish the book.
8. His sister is up to page 353.
9. She needs to read 337 pages to finish the book.
10. It will take her 34 days.

SOLUTIONS

Note: Many solutions are written statements rather than just numbers. This is to encourage teachers and pupils to solve problems in this way.

FARM TRAILS ....Page 49

1. 10 200 m or 10 km 200 m
2. 3370 cm or 33 m 70 cm

BALANCING ....Page 50

1. 7 lychees
2. £2.40
3. 30 pence

roll	6 rolls	loaf	4 rolls	2 loaves	Total
6 rolls and 1 loaf costs £4.20					
0.50	3.00	1.20	2.00	2.40	5.40 – too little
0.40	2.40	1.80	1.60	3.60	5.20 – too little
0.35	2.10	2.10	1.40	4.20	5.60 – too much
0.30	1.80	2.40	1.20	4.80	6.00
A loaf of bread costs £2.40. A bread roll costs 30p.					

SQUARES AND AREA ....Page 51

1. 36 cm²
2. 64 cm²
3. 80 cm²

DVD RENTALS..................................Page 53

DVD Easy		Hours open
Monday	CLOSED	0
Tuesday	11:00 am to 8:00 pm	9
Wednesday	11:00 am to 9:00 pm	10
Thursday	10:00 am to 9:00 pm	11
Friday	11:00 am to 10:00 pm	11
Saturday	10:00 am to 10:00 pm	12
Sunday	11:00 am to 9:00 pm	10
	Total hours	**63**

DVD Rentals		Hours open
Monday	11:00 am to 9:00 pm	10
Tuesday	11:00 am to 9:00 pm	10
Wednesday	CLOSED	0
Thursday	11:00 am to 9:00 pm	10
Friday	11:00 am to 11:00 pm	12
Saturday	10:00 am to 11:00 pm	13
Sunday	11:00 am to 9:00 pm	10
	Total hours	**65**

1. 2 hours
2. 11:00 pm
3. 10:00 am
4. DVD Rentals
5. Saturday
6. either store
7. DVD Rentals
8. (a) No (b) Yes (c) Yes (d) Yes (e) No

DRIVE TIME...................................Page 54

1. (a) **Car One**

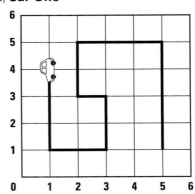

(b) **Car Two**

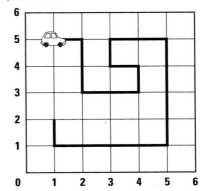

2. (a) (4, 4) (3, 4) (3, 5) (1, 5) (1, 3) (3, 3) (3, 2) (1, 2) (1, 1) (4, 1) (4, 3) (6, 3)
   (b) (6, 4) (3, 4) (3, 6) (1, 6) (1, 3) (2, 3) (2, 1) (4, 1) (4, 5)
3. Answers will vary

CLOCK WATCHING ....Page 55

1. (a) 0:12, 0:21, 0:19, 0:29, 1:02, 1:20, 1:09, 1:29, 2:01, 2:10, 2:09, 2:19, 9:01, 9:10, 9:12, 9:21, 9:02, 9:20, 10:29, 12:09, 19:02, 19:20, 20:19
   (b) 12:09
   (c) 0:12
2. (a) 16
   (b) 384
   (c) 7
3. 391

SOLUTIONS

Note: *Many solutions are written statements rather than just numbers. This is to encourage teachers and pupils to solve problems in this way.*

ON THE FARM...**Page 57**
1. 26 emus and 12 alpacas
2. 4 calves and 6 piglets
3. 15 alpacas and 30 emus

IN THE BARN..**Page 58**
1. three wheels = 14, two wheels = 11
2. 13 spiders and 16 beetles
3. Answers will vary as there are multiple answers.
   Answers are displayed in the table:

Number of cows	Number of chickens	Number of legs
6	2	28
5	4	28
4	6	28
3	8	28
2	10	28
1	12	28

MARKET DAY..**Page 59**
1. She paid £275 for the pig.
2. The cow sold for £379.
3. £150

SHOPPING..**Page 61**
1. £180
2. £81

ISOMETRIC RESOURCE PAGE

0–99 BOARD RESOURCE PAGE

0	1	2	3	4	5	6	7	8	9
10	11	12	13	14	15	16	17	18	19
20	21	22	23	24	25	26	27	28	29
30	31	32	33	34	35	36	37	38	39
40	41	42	43	44	45	46	47	48	49
50	51	52	53	54	55	56	57	58	59
60	61	62	63	64	65	66	67	68	69
70	71	72	73	74	75	76	77	78	79
80	81	82	83	84	85	86	87	88	89
90	91	92	93	94	95	96	97	98	99

4-DIGIT NUMBER EXPANDER RESOURCE PAGE (x 5)

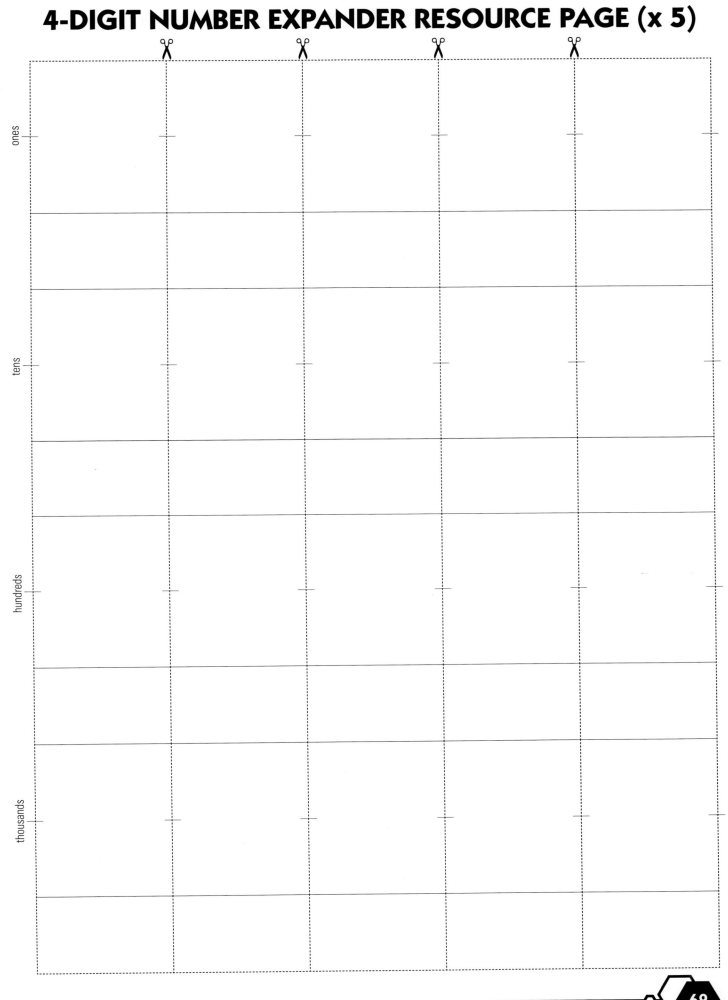

10 mm x 10 mm GRID RESOURCE PAGE

Problem-solving in mathematics

www.prim-ed.com   Prim-Ed Publishing®

15 mm x 15 mm GRID RESOURCE PAGE

Prim-Ed Publishing®   www.prim-ed.com

Problem-solving in mathematics

TRIANGULAR GRID RESOURCE PAGE

www.prim-ed.com   Prim-Ed Publishing®